Scott Foresman
Grade 4
Unit and End-of-Year
Benchmark Tests
Teacher's Manual

Reading STREET

Grade 4

PEARSON

Glenview, Illinois • Boston, Massachusetts • Chandler, Arizona • Upper Saddle River, New Jersey

The Pearson Promise

As the largest educational publishing company in the world, Pearson is committed to providing you with curriculum that not only meets the Common Core State Standards, but also supports your implementation of these standards with your students.

Pearson has aligned the Common Core State Standards to every grade level of *Scott Foresman Reading Street,* our premier educational curriculum. This product provides an alignment of the Common Core State Standards to the Grade 4 assessment items in *Scott Foresman Reading Street Unit and End-of-Year Benchmark Tests.*

We value your partnership highly and look forward to continuing our mission to provide educational materials that fully satisfy your classroom needs.

ISBN-13: 978-0-328-68394-9
ISBN-10:   0-328-68394-9

10 V056 15

Contents

    Unit 1

    Unit 2

    Unit 3

    Unit 4

    Unit 5

    Unit 6

    End-of-Year

Contents

OVERVIEW

Scott Foresman *Reading Street* provides a wide array of formal tests and classroom assessments to support instruction. Formal assessments include the following:

- Baseline Group Tests

- Weekly Selection Tests

- Fresh Reads for Differentiated Test Practice

- Unit and End-of-Year Benchmark Tests aligned to Common Core State Standards

This Teacher's Manual provides information for administering the Benchmark Tests, scoring the tests, and interpreting the results. Detailed information about other assessment materials and procedures may be found in the *Assessment Handbook*.

Description of the Benchmark Tests

In Grade 4, there are six Unit Benchmark Tests—one for each unit—and an End-of-Year Test. The Unit Benchmark Tests are designed to measure student progress based on the comprehension skills and strategies, literary elements, vocabulary, writing conventions, and types of writing taught in each unit. The End-of-Year Benchmark Test measures skills covered in all six units. The Benchmark Tests offer an integrated approach to assessment by measuring all skills and strategies in relation to reading selections.

In addition, the Benchmark Tests are designed to provide practice in test-taking skills and to prepare students to take the Reading/Language Arts section of standardized tests, state tests, or teacher-made tests. The tests include both multiple-choice and constructed-response questions. They also include writing prompts that will help students prepare for state writing tests.

Each Unit Benchmark Test has these features:

- Each test has two components—Reading – Parts 1–3 and Writing – Part 4.

- Reading – Part 1 presents two selections in different genres. The genres of these selections, drawn from fiction and nonfiction, reflect genres taught in each unit.

- Each selection reflects the theme of the unit.

- Reading – Parts 1–3 contain forty multiple-choice questions and two constructed-response questions. These questions test reading comprehension, literary elements, critical thinking skills, vocabulary strategies, and writing conventions. Some of the items measure the ability to synthesize information and to compare and contrast across texts.

- Writing – Part 4 of each test presents a writing prompt based on one of the types of writing taught in the unit. These prompts are similar to those found in state writing tests.

The End-of-Year Benchmark Test follows the same design as the Unit Benchmark Tests, but it has more items. It measures selected skills from all six units taught during the year.

The Benchmark Tests are designed to assess student progress at the end of each unit and at the end of the school year. Selections and questions in the Unit Benchmark Tests become progressively more difficult from Unit 1 to Unit 6 to reflect the increasing sophistication of materials students are able to handle.

ADMINISTERING THE TESTS

The Benchmark Tests are designed for group administration. You may decide to administer each test in one sitting, or you may administer parts of the test in two or more sittings. (If you administer the test in two or more sittings, try to schedule the sittings on the same day or within a day of the previous sitting because some of the questions at the end of the test compare and contrast selections.)

These tests were also designed to give teachers the option of separating multiple-choice questions from the constructed-response questions. You may opt to have students skip the constructed-response questions in order to create an all multiple-choice test.

These tests are not intended to be timed. We recommend allowing ample time for all students to complete the tests at their own pace. However, for the purposes of scheduling, planning, and practicing timed-test situations, the chart below shows the number of items in each test part and the estimated amount of time required to complete each part.

Test Part	Number of Items	Estimated Time
Reading – Part 1 (Selection 1)	11 multiple-choice	20–25 minutes
	1 constructed-response	5 minutes
Reading – Part 1 (Selection 2)	11 multiple-choice	20–25 minutes
	1 constructed-response	5 minutes
Reading – Part 2 (Vocabulary)	10 multiple-choice	20 minutes
Reading – Part 3 Writing Conventions OPTIONAL	8 multiple-choice	15–20 minutes
Writing – Part 4 OPTIONAL	1 writing prompt	45 minutes

The End-of-Year Benchmark Test has more selections, sixty multiple-choice items, two constructed-response items, and one writing prompt. To administer the End-of-Year Test, plan on about two hours for Reading – Parts 1–3 and forty-five minutes for Writing – Part 4.

Directions for Administering the Tests

Before you administer a test . . .

Review the test directions below and on pages T8–T9. Modify the directions as needed based on how you decide to administer each test. For Reading – Parts 1–3, students can mark their responses directly on their tests or on the Bubble Answer Sheets included for copy on pages T57–T58. In Writing – Part 4 of all tests, students write compositions in response to a prompt. They write their compositions on the lined pages in their test booklets. You may wish to provide scrap paper that students can use to plan their writing. Only the writing in their test booklets will be scored.

When you are ready to administer a test . . .

Distribute a test to each student. Have students write their names on the front of their test booklets, their answer sheets, and on any additional sheets of paper they may use. Have students flip through the test as you point out and explain its key features. For example, point out directions, selection titles, selections, art, Go On and Stop symbols, multiple-choice questions with answer choices, constructed-response questions with lines for written responses, and the writing prompts with checklists and two lined pages for the compositions. Allow time for students to ask any questions they may have about the test's contents before you begin the test.

Directions in **bold** type that follow are intended to be read aloud. Other directions are intended for your information only. For Reading – Part 1, modify the general directions as needed if you intend to skip the constructed-response questions. For Writing – Part 4, you may wish to modify directions about the amount of time suggested for the testing session to match the time allowed for your state's writing tests.

Directions for Reading – Part 1: Comprehension

In the first part of this test, you will read two selections and answer some questions about them. There are two types of questions: multiple-choice questions and questions that require you to write short answers.

If you are having students mark their answers to the multiple-choice questions directly on their tests, then say:

Mark your answers to the multiple-choice questions in your test. For each question, circle the letter that goes with the answer you choose. If you want to change your answer, completely erase the circle you made and circle a different letter. Do not make any other marks in your test.

If students are marking their answers to the multiple-choice questions on answer sheets, then say:

Mark your answers to the multiple-choice questions on your answer sheet. For each question, fill in the circle on your answer sheet that goes with the answer you choose. Fill in the circle completely and make your mark heavy and dark. If you want to change your answer, completely erase the mark you made and fill in a different circle. Do not make any other marks on your answer sheet.

For all students, say:

For Questions A and B, write your answers on the lines in your test. Think carefully and write your ideas as clearly as you can. Allow about five minutes to answer each of these questions.

Read the directions carefully. You can ask me to explain any directions you do not understand. Read the selections and the questions very carefully. You may look back at a selection as often as you like to help you answer the questions.

Answer the questions you are sure about first. If a question seems too difficult, skip it, and go back to it later. Check each answer to make sure it is the best answer for the question asked.

Think positively. Some questions may seem hard, but others will be easy. Relax. Most people get nervous about tests. It's natural. Just do your best.

Continue with Reading – Part 1: Comprehension until you come to a STOP sign at the end of Question B. When you have completed that question, put your pencils down, close your test booklets, and look up.

Tell students how much of the test they are expected to complete in this sitting and how much time they have to complete their work. Allow time for students to ask any questions about the directions. Then direct students to open their tests to a specified page and begin. You may wish to give students a break upon completion of this part of the test.

Directions for Reading – Part 2 and Part 3 (Optional)

Read aloud the directions from the student book for Parts 2 and 3. Tell students how much time they have to complete their work for each part of the test. Point out the STOP signs at the end of each part, instructing them to put their pencils down and look up whenever they come to a STOP sign. That way, you can wait for all students to complete the section before moving on to the next part.

Directions for Writing – Part 4 (Optional)

For the last part of the test, you will do a writing exercise. The writing prompt in your test explains what you are going to write about and gives you some ideas for planning your writing. Before you begin writing, think about what you want to say and how you want to say it. You can use scrap paper to jot down your ideas.

Benchmark Test Teacher's Manual

After planning what you will write, write your composition on the two lined pages in your test. Be sure that your writing does what the prompt asks you to do. Only the writing in your test booklet will be scored.

Your writing may be about something that is real or make-believe, but remember, you are to write ONLY about the prompt in your test.

You may give your writing a title if you would like. However, a title is not required.

You may NOT use a dictionary. If you do not know how to spell a word, sound out the word and do the best you can.

You may either print or write in cursive. It is important to write as neatly as possible.

Your writing should be easy to read and should show that you can organize and express your thoughts clearly and completely.

I cannot read the prompt to you or help you plan what to write. You must read and plan yourself. Remember to read the prompt first and then plan what you will write.

You have a total of forty-five minutes to read, plan, and respond to your prompt. I will let you know when you have ten minutes left. (You may wish to modify the amount of time you allow for Writing – Part 4 to match the time allowed on your state's writing tests.)

If you finish early, please proofread your composition. Revise and edit the writing in your test. Use the questions in the Checklist for Writers to help you check your composition.

Allow time for students to ask any questions about the directions. Then direct students to open their tests to the writing prompt page, read the prompt, plan their writing, and write their compositions. Be sure to alert students when they have ten minutes left.

After testing . . .

Once students are finished testing, collect all test booklets and/or answer sheets. Directions for scoring the tests begin on page T10. The answer keys begin on page T46. Evaluation charts with alignments to Common Core State Standards (pages T31–T44) are provided along with a class record chart on page T45.

SCORING THE TESTS

The Benchmark Tests are intended to be scored by part—a total score for Reading – Parts 1–3 and a separate score for Writing – Part 4. To make scoring easier, copy and use the following charts as needed:

- the Unit Benchmark Test Evaluation Charts, beginning on page T31, for recording a student's individual scores on a Unit Benchmark Test;

- the End-of-Year Benchmark Test Evaluation Chart, on pages T43 and T44, for recording a student's individual scores on the End-of-Year Benchmark Test;

- the Class Record Chart, on page T45, for recording test scores for all students for all six units.

Answer keys for each test begin on page T47. In Reading – Part 1, there are two types of items: multiple-choice questions and constructed-response questions. These types of items are scored in slightly different ways, as explained below. In Writing – Part 4, each prompt is linked to one of four different types of writing: narrative, descriptive, expository, or persuasive. For each type of writing, there are four Writing Scoring Rubrics. Each rubric has a different point scale. Choose the rubric that most closely matches the rubric for your state's writing tests or the rubric you deem most appropriate for your students. Writing Scoring Rubrics begin on page T12.

Scoring Multiple-Choice Questions

Each multiple-choice question has four answer choices labeled A, B, C, D or F, G, H, J. Refer to the answer key for the test you are scoring and mark each multiple-choice question as either 1 (correct) or 0 (incorrect).

Scoring Constructed-Response Questions

Use the answer keys and the rubric on page T11 to help you score constructed-response questions. Award each constructed-response answer a score from 0 to 2 points, depending on how accurate and complete the response is. The answer keys provide abbreviated descriptions of top responses. Have an ideal top response in mind before you assess students' responses.

Constructed-Response Scoring Rubric

Points	Description
2	The response indicates a **full understanding** of the question's reading or critical-thinking skill. The response is accurate and complete. Necessary support and/or examples are included, and the information is clearly text-based.
1	The response indicates a **partial understanding** of the question's reading or critical-thinking skill. The response includes information that is essentially correct and text-based, but it is too general or too simplistic. Some of the support and/or examples may be incomplete or omitted.
0	The response is **inaccurate,** confused, and/or irrelevant, or the student has failed to respond to the task.

Scoring Writing – Part 4

To evaluate students' responses to a writing prompt, familiarize yourself with the writing prompt, and review the Writing Scoring Rubrics on pages T12–T19. Identify the type of writing suggested in the writing prompt. (Types of writing for each prompt are identified in the answer keys that begin on page T47.) Then choose one of the four Writing Scoring Rubrics provided for that type of writing. Use the rubric to score each composition on a scale from 1 to 6, 1 to 5, 1 to 4, or 1 to 3.

Writing Scoring Rubrics: Narrative Writing

6-Point Scoring Rubric

6	5	4	3	2	1
narrative writing is well focused on the topic	narrative writing is focused on the topic	narrative writing is generally focused on the topic	narrative writing is generally focused but may stray from the topic	narrative writing is minimally related to the topic	narrative writing is not focused on the topic
contains clear ideas	most ideas are clear	ideas are generally clear	ideas may be somewhat unclear	ideas are often unclear	ideas are unclear
logically organized; uses transitions	logically organized; uses some transitions	logically organized with some lapses; has transitions	somewhat organized; may lack transitions	minimally organized; no transitions	unorganized; no transitions
voice is engaging; well suited to purpose and audience	voice comes through well; suited to purpose and audience	voice comes through occasionally; suited to purpose and audience	voice uneven; not always suited to purpose or audience	slight evidence of voice; little sense of purpose or audience	weak voice; no sense of purpose or audience
demonstrates varied, precise word choice	generally demonstrates varied, precise word choice	often demonstrates varied, precise word choice	word choice could be more varied, precise	poor choice of words; limited vocabulary	limited vocabulary
sentences are complete, fluent, and varied	most sentences are complete and varied	many sentences are complete and varied	some incomplete sentences; little variety	sentences are incomplete; show little or no variety	gross errors in sentence structure; no variety
shows excellent control of writing conventions	shows very good control of writing conventions	shows good control of writing conventions	shows fair control of writing conventions	shows frequent errors in writing conventions	shows many serious errors in writing conventions

5-Point Scoring Rubric

5	4	3	2	1
narrative writing is well focused on the topic	narrative writing is focused on the topic	narrative writing is generally focused on the topic	narrative writing strays from the topic	narrative writing is not focused on the topic
contains clear ideas	most ideas are clear	ideas are generally clear	many ideas are unclear	ideas are unclear
logically organized; uses transitions	logically organized; uses some transitions	logically organized with some lapses; transitions weak	little organization; few or no transitions	unorganized; no transitions
voice is engaging; well suited to purpose and audience	voice is fairly strong; suited to purpose and audience	voice comes through occasionally; may not suit purpose or audience	voice comes through rarely; poorly suited to purpose or audience	weak voice; no sense of audience or purpose
demonstrates varied, precise word choice	generally demonstrates varied, precise word choice	word choice could be more varied, precise	poor choice of words; limited vocabulary	choice of words very limited
sentences are complete, fluent, and varied	most sentences are complete and varied	many sentences are complete; generally varied	incomplete sentences; little variety	incomplete sentences; no variety
shows excellent control of writing conventions	shows very good control of writing conventions	shows fairly good control of writing conventions	shows frequent errors in writing conventions	shows many serious errors in writing conventions

Writing Scoring Rubrics: Narrative Writing

4-Point Scoring Rubric

4	3	2	1
narrative writing is well focused on the topic	narrative writing is focused on the topic	narrative writing may stray from the topic	narrative writing is not focused on the topic
contains clear ideas	most ideas are clear	some ideas may be unclear	ideas are unclear
logically organized; uses transitions	logically organized; uses some transitions	little organization; may be few or no transitions	unorganized; no transitions
voice is engaging; well suited to purpose and audience	voice is fairly strong; suited to purpose and audience	slight evidence of voice; may be poorly suited to purpose or audience	weak voice; no sense of audience or purpose
demonstrates varied, precise word choice	generally demonstrates varied, precise word choice	choice of words limited	choice of words very limited
sentences are complete, fluent, and varied	most sentences are complete and varied	many incomplete sentences; little variety	mostly incomplete sentences; no variety
shows excellent control of writing conventions	shows very good control of writing conventions	shows frequent errors in writing conventions	shows many serious errors in writing conventions

3-Point Scoring Rubric

3	2	1
narrative writing is well focused on the topic	narrative writing is generally focused on the topic	narrative writing is not focused on the topic
contains clear ideas	ideas are sometimes unclear	ideas are unclear
logically organized; uses transitions	logically organized with lapses; transitions need improvement	unorganized; no transitions
voice is engaging; well suited to purpose and audience	voice comes through fairly well; may not suit purpose or audience	weak voice; no sense of audience
demonstrates varied, precise word choice	word choice could be more varied, precise	choice of words very limited
sentences are complete, fluent, and varied	some sentences are complete and varied	incomplete sentences; no variety
shows excellent control of writing conventions	shows fair control of writing conventions	shows many serious errors in writing conventions

Writing Scoring Rubrics: Descriptive Writing

6-Point Scoring Rubric

6	5	4	3	2	1
descriptive writing is well focused on the topic	descriptive writing is focused on the topic	descriptive writing is generally focused on the topic	descriptive writing may stray from the topic	descriptive writing is minimally related to the topic	descriptive writing is not focused on the topic
contains clear ideas	most ideas are clear	ideas are generally clear	ideas may be somewhat unclear	ideas are often unclear	ideas are unclear
logically organized; uses transitions	logically organized; uses some transitions	logically organized with some lapses; has transitions	somewhat organized; may lack transitions	minimally organized; no transitions	unorganized; no transitions
voice is engaging; well suited to purpose and audience	voice comes through well; suited to purpose and audience	voice comes through occasionally; suited to purpose and audience	voice uneven; not always suited to purpose or audience	slight evidence of voice; little sense of purpose or audience	weak voice; no sense of purpose or audience
precise, vivid language paints strong pictures	generally demonstrates varied, precise word choice	often demonstrates varied, precise word choice	word choice could be more varied, precise	poor choice of words; limited vocabulary	limited vocabulary
sentences are complete, fluent, and varied	most sentences are complete and varied	many sentences are complete and varied	some incomplete sentences; little variety	sentences are incomplete; show little or no variety	gross errors in sentence structure; no variety
shows excellent control of writing conventions	shows very good control of writing conventions	shows good control of writing conventions	shows fair control of writing conventions	shows frequent errors in writing conventions	shows many serious errors in writing conventions

5-Point Scoring Rubric

5	4	3	2	1
descriptive writing is well focused on the topic	descriptive writing is focused on the topic	descriptive writing is generally focused on the topic	descriptive writing strays from the topic	descriptive writing is not focused on the topic
contains clear ideas	most ideas are clear	ideas are generally clear	many ideas are unclear	ideas are unclear
logically organized; uses transitions	logically organized; uses some transitions	logically organized with some lapses; transitions weak	little organization; few or no transitions	unorganized; no transitions
voice is engaging; well suited to purpose and audience	voice is fairly engaging; suited to purpose and audience	voice comes through occasionally; may not suit purpose or audience	voice comes through rarely; poorly suited to purpose or audience	weak voice; no sense of audience or purpose
demonstrates varied, precise word choice	generally demonstrates varied, precise word choice	word choice could be more varied, precise	poor word choice; limited vocabulary	word choice very limited
sentences are complete, fluent, and varied	most sentences are complete and varied	many sentences are complete; generally varied	incomplete sentences; little variety	incomplete sentences; no variety
shows excellent control of writing conventions	shows very good control of writing conventions	shows fairly good control of writing conventions	shows frequent errors in writing conventions	shows many serious errors in writing conventions

4 Copyright © Pearson Education, Inc., or its affiliates. All Rights Reserved.

Writing Scoring Rubrics: Descriptive Writing

4-Point Scoring Rubric			
4	**3**	**2**	**1**
descriptive writing is well focused on the topic	descriptive writing is focused on the topic	descriptive writing may stray from the topic	descriptive writing is not focused on the topic
contains clear ideas	most ideas are clear	some ideas may be unclear	ideas are unclear
logically organized; uses transitions	logically organized; uses some transitions	little organization; may be few or no transitions	unorganized; no transitions
voice is engaging; well suited to purpose and audience	voice is fairly engaging; suited to purpose and audience	slight evidence of voice; may be poorly suited to audience or purpose	weak voice; no sense of audience or purpose
demonstrates varied, precise word choice	generally demonstrates varied, precise word choice	choice of words limited	word choice very limited
sentences are complete, fluent, and varied	most sentences are complete and varied	many incomplete sentences; little variety	mostly incomplete sentences; no variety
shows excellent control of writing conventions	shows very good control of writing conventions	shows frequent errors in writing conventions	shows many serious errors in writing conventions

3-Point Scoring Rubric		
3	**2**	**1**
descriptive writing is well focused on the topic	descriptive writing is generally focused on the topic	descriptive writing is not focused on the topic
contains clear ideas	ideas are sometimes unclear	ideas are unclear
logically organized; uses transitions	logically organized with lapses; transitions need improvement	unorganized; no transitions
voice is engaging; well suited to purpose and audience	voice comes through fairly well; may not suit purpose or audience	weak voice; no sense of purpose or audience
demonstrates varied, precise word choice	word choice could be more varied, precise	choice of words very limited
sentences are complete, fluent, and varied	some sentences are complete and varied	incomplete sentences; no variety
shows excellent control of writing conventions	shows fair control of writing conventions	shows many serious errors in writing conventions

Writing Scoring Rubrics: Expository Writing

6-Point Scoring Rubric

6	5	4	3	2	1
expository writing is well focused on the topic	expository writing is focused on the topic	expository writing is generally focused on the topic	expository writing may stray from the topic	expository writing is minimally related to the topic	expository writing is not focused on the topic
contains clear ideas	most ideas are clear	ideas are generally clear	ideas may be somewhat unclear	ideas are often unclear	ideas are unclear
logically organized; uses transitions	logically organized; uses some transitions	logically organized with some lapses; has transitions	little organization; may lack transitions	minimally organized; no transitions	unorganized; no transitions
voice is engaging; well suited to purpose and audience	voice comes through well; suited to purpose and audience	voice comes through occasionally; suited to purpose and audience	voice uneven; not always suited to purpose or audience	slight evidence of voice; little sense of purpose or audience	weak voice; no sense of purpose or audience
demonstrates varied, precise word choice	generally demonstrates varied, precise word choice	often demonstrates varied, precise word choice	word choice could be more varied, precise	poor choice of words; limited vocabulary	limited vocabulary
sentences are complete, fluent, and varied	most sentences are complete and varied	many sentences are complete and varied	some incomplete sentences; little variety	sentences are incomplete; show little or no variety	gross errors in sentence structure; no variety
shows excellent control of writing conventions	shows very good control of writing conventions	shows good control of writing conventions	shows fair control of writing conventions	shows frequent errors in writing conventions	shows many serious errors in writing conventions

5-Point Scoring Rubric

5	4	3	2	1
expository writing is well focused on the topic	expository writing is focused on the topic	expository writing is generally focused on the topic	expository writing strays from the topic	expository writing is not focused on the topic
contains clear ideas	most ideas are clear	ideas are generally clear	many ideas are unclear	ideas are unclear
logically organized; uses transitions	logically organized; uses some transitions	logically organized with some lapses; transitions weak	little organization; few or no transitions	unorganized; no transitions
voice is engaging; well suited to purpose and audience	voice is fairly engaging; suited to purpose and audience	voice comes through occasionally; may not suit purpose or audience	voice comes through rarely; poorly suited to purpose or audience	weak voice; no sense of audience or purpose
demonstrates varied, precise word choice	generally demonstrates varied, precise word choice	word choice could be more varied, precise	poor word choice; limited vocabulary	word choice very limited
sentences are complete, fluent, and varied	most sentences are complete and varied	many sentences are complete; generally varied	incomplete sentences; little variety	incomplete sentences; no variety
shows excellent control of writing conventions	shows very good control of writing conventions	shows fairly good control of writing conventions	shows frequent errors in writing conventions	shows many serious errors in writing conventions

Benchmark Test Teacher's Manual

Writing Scoring Rubrics: Expository Writing

4-Point Scoring Rubric			
4	**3**	**2**	**1**
expository writing is well focused on the topic	expository writing is focused on the topic	expository writing may stray from the topic	expository writing is not focused on the topic
contains clear ideas	most ideas are clear	some ideas may be unclear	ideas are unclear
logically organized; uses transitions	logically organized; uses some transitions	little organization; may be few or no transitions	unorganized; no transitions
voice is engaging; well suited to purpose and audience	voice is fairly engaging; suited to purpose and audience	slight evidence of voice; may be poorly suited to audience or purpose	weak voice; no sense of audience or purpose
demonstrates varied, precise word choice	generally demonstrates varied, precise word choice	choice of words limited	word choice very limited
sentences are complete, fluent, and varied	most sentences are complete and varied	many incomplete sentences; little variety	mostly incomplete sentences; no variety
shows excellent control of writing conventions	shows very good control of writing conventions	shows frequent errors in writing conventions	shows many serious errors in writing conventions

3-Point Scoring Rubric		
3	**2**	**1**
expository writing is well focused on the topic	expository writing is generally focused on the topic	expository writing is not focused on the topic
contains clear ideas	ideas are sometimes unclear	ideas are unclear
logically organized; uses transitions	logically organized with lapses; transitions need improvement	unorganized; no transitions
voice is engaging; well suited to purpose and audience	voice comes through fairly well; may not suit purpose or audience	weak voice; no sense of purpose or audience
demonstrates varied, precise word choice	word choice could be more varied, precise	choice of words very limited
sentences are complete, fluent, and varied	some sentences are complete and varied	incomplete sentences; no variety
shows excellent control of writing conventions	shows fair control of writing conventions	shows many serious errors in writing conventions

Writing Scoring Rubrics: Persuasive Writing

6-Point Scoring Rubric

6	5	4	3	2	1
persuasive writing is well focused on the topic	persuasive writing is focused on the topic	persuasive writing is generally focused on the topic	persuasive writing is generally focused but may stray from the topic	persuasive writing is minimally related to the topic	persuasive writing is not focused on the topic
contains clear ideas	most ideas are clear	ideas are generally clear	ideas may be somewhat unclear	ideas are often unclear	ideas are unclear
presents reasons in order; uses transitions	presents reasons in some order; uses some transitions	presents most reasons in order; has transitions	reasons may not be in proper order; may lack transitions	reasons are not in order; no transitions	reasons, if any, are not in order; no transitions
voice is engaging; well suited to purpose and audience	voice comes through well; suited to purpose and audience	voice comes through occasionally; suited to purpose and audience	voice uneven; not always suited to purpose or audience	slight evidence of voice; little sense of audience or purpose	weak voice; no sense of purpose or audience
demonstrates precise, persuasive wording	generally demonstrates precise, persuasive word choice	often demonstrates precise, persuasive word choice	word choice is not always precise or persuasive	poor choice of words; not very persuasive	limited vocabulary; fails to persuade
sentences are complete, fluent, and varied	most sentences are complete and varied	many sentences are complete and varied	some incomplete sentences; little variety	sentences are incomplete; show little or no variety	gross errors in sentence structure; no variety
shows excellent control of writing conventions	shows very good control of writing conventions	shows good control of writing conventions	shows fair control of writing conventions	shows frequent errors in writing conventions	shows many serious errors in writing conventions

5-Point Scoring Rubric

5	4	3	2	1
persuasive writing is well focused on the topic	persuasive writing is focused on the topic	persuasive writing is generally focused on the topic	persuasive writing strays from the topic	persuasive writing is not focused on the topic
contains clear ideas	most ideas are clear	ideas are generally clear	many ideas are unclear	ideas are unclear
presents reasons in order; uses transitions	presents reasons in some order; uses some transitions	presents most reasons in order; transitions weak	reasons are not in order; few or no transitions	reasons, if any, are not in order; no transitions
voice is engaging; well suited to purpose and audience	voice is fairly engaging; suited to purpose and audience	voice comes through occasionally; may not suit purpose or audience	voice comes through rarely; poorly suited to audience or purpose	weak voice; no sense of audience or purpose
demonstrates precise, persuasive wording	generally demonstrates precise, persuasive word choice	word choice could be more precise, persuasive	word choice limited; not persuasive	word choice very limited; fails to persuade
sentences are complete, fluent, and varied	most sentences are complete and varied	many sentences are complete; generally varied	incomplete sentences; little variety	incomplete sentences; no variety
shows excellent control of writing conventions	shows very good control of writing conventions	shows fairly good control of writing conventions	shows frequent errors in writing conventions	shows many serious errors in writing conventions

Writing Scoring Rubrics: Persuasive Writing

4-Point Scoring Rubric

4	3	2	1
persuasive writing is well focused on the topic	persuasive writing is focused on the topic	persuasive writing may stray from the topic	persuasive writing is not focused on the topic
contains clear ideas	most ideas are clear	some ideas may be unclear	ideas are unclear
presents reasons in order; uses transitions	presents reasons in some order; uses some transitions	reasons may not be in order; may be few or no transitions	reasons, if any, are not in order; no transitions
voice is engaging; well suited to purpose and audience	voice is fairly engaging; suited to purpose and audience	slight evidence of voice; may be poorly suited to purpose or audience	weak voice; no sense of audience or purpose
demonstrates precise, persuasive wording	generally demonstrates precise, persuasive word choice	choice of words limited; not very persuasive	word choice very limited; fails to persuade
sentences are complete, fluent, and varied	most sentences are complete and varied	many incomplete sentences; little variety	many incomplete sentences; no variety
shows excellent control of writing conventions	shows very good control of writing conventions	shows frequent errors in writing conventions	shows many serious errors in writing conventions

3-Point Scoring Rubric

3	2	1
persuasive writing is well focused on the topic	persuasive writing is generally focused on the topic	persuasive writing is not focused on the topic
contains clear ideas	ideas are sometimes unclear	ideas are unclear
logically organized; presents reasons in order	logically organized with lapses; presents most reasons in order	unorganized; reasons, if any, are not in order
voice is engaging; well suited to purpose and audience	voice comes through fairly well; may not suit audience or purpose	weak voice; no sense of audience or purpose
demonstrates precise, persuasive word choice	word choice could be more precise, persuasive	choice of words very limited; fails to persuade
sentences are complete, fluent, and varied	some sentences are complete and varied	incomplete sentences; no variety
shows excellent control of writing conventions	shows fair control of writing conventions	shows many serious errors in writing conventions

Using an Evaluation Chart

Use the Evaluation Charts beginning on page T31 to score the Unit Benchmark Tests and the End-of-Year Benchmark Test. To score one of these tests use the following procedure:

1. Make a copy of the appropriate Evaluation Chart for each student.

2. To score Reading – Parts 1–3, circle the score for each item on the Evaluation Chart. Multiple-choice questions are scored 0 (incorrect) or 1 (correct). Constructed-response questions are scored 0, 1, or 2 points. Use the answer key for the test you are scoring and the Constructed-Response Scoring Rubric on page T11 to help you score the Reading parts of the test.

3. Find the student's total score for Reading – Parts 1–3 by adding the individual scores for all items.

4. Use the formula on the Evaluation Chart to find the percentage score for Reading – Parts 1–3 by dividing the total *obtained* score by the total *possible* score and then multiplying the quotient by 100.

5. To score Writing – Part 4, identify the type of writing suggested in the prompt and choose one of the four Writing Scoring Rubrics (pages T12–T19) for that type of writing. Read the student's writing and score each composition on a scale from 1 to 6, 1 to 5, 1 to 4, or 1 to 3.

6. Mark the student's Writing score on the Evaluation Chart. Add any notes or observations about the writing that may be helpful to you and the student in later instruction.

INTERPRETING TEST RESULTS

A student's score on a Benchmark Test provides only one look at the student's progress and should be interpreted in conjunction with other assessments and the teacher's observations. However, a low score on one or both parts of a Benchmark Test probably indicates a need for closer review of the student's performance and perhaps additional instruction.

Regrouping for Instruction

The Unit Benchmark Tests can help you make regrouping decisions. In Grade 4 there are opportunities for regrouping at the end of Units 2, 3, 4, 5, and 6. Depending on each student's progress, teachers may prefer to regroup more or less frequently.

Students who score 65% or below on the multiple-choice items of the Comprehension and Vocabulary sections of the Benchmark Tests and who typically demonstrate unsatisfactory work on assignments and in classroom discussions would benefit from being in the Strategic Intervention reading group for the next unit of instruction.

Students who score between 66% and 90% on the multiple-choice items of the Comprehension and Vocabulary sections of the Benchmark Tests and who meet other criteria, such as consistently satisfactory work on assignments and in classroom discussions, likely belong in the On-Level reading group for the next unit of instruction. Students in the low end of that range should be observed carefully and may need on-going assistance, extra instruction, and opportunities for further practice, just as students in the Strategic Intervention group do. Students in the upper end of that range should receive their instruction and practice with on-level materials, but they may need extra challenge and enrichment, just as students in the Advanced reading group do.

Students who score 91% or above on the multiple-choice items of the Comprehension and Vocabulary sections of the Benchmark Tests and who meet other criteria, such as consistently excellent performance on assigned paperwork and in classroom discussions, are capable of work in the Advanced reading group for the next unit of instruction. They should be given multiple opportunities to engage in enrichment activities and real-world investigations.

Further Analysis of Results

Each Reading (Parts 1–3) item on an Evaluation Chart is linked to a tested skill and a Common Core State Standard. By identifying which items the student answered incorrectly and referring to the list of tested skills, you may be able to determine specific skills or areas in which the student needs additional help. For example, if the student answers six questions incorrectly and several involve literary elements such as plot and character, you may want to plan additional instruction for the student in this area. While the Benchmark Tests do not provide sufficient context coverage of individual skills to be truly "diagnostic," students' performance patterns can often provide useful clues as to particular strengths and weaknesses.

Grading: For more information on how to use a writing assessment scale as an element in determining classroom grades, refer to the "Grading Writing" section of the *Assessment Handbook.*

ASSISTING ENGLISH LANGUAGE LEARNERS

While the Benchmark Tests provide teachers with a way to measure students' progress on a unit-by-unit basis, Benchmark Tests also provide an opportunity for teachers to help English language learners become familiar with the linguistic patterns and structures they will encounter while taking state tests. The format of the Benchmark Tests is similar to the format of the state tests, with similar direction lines, question stems, answer formats, and markings to "stop" and "go on."

Among assessment tools, standardized tests cause teachers of English language learners the most concern. State tests, considered "high stakes," may be used to evaluate the effectiveness of the curriculum, the teacher, or the instructional approach. They are used to evaluate students' overall progress. High-stakes tests are typically designed and normed for proficient speakers of English. By providing opportunities for English language learners to become familiar with the formats and language of the Benchmark Tests, teachers assist students in obtaining results that reflect students' learning of the content rather than their aptitude for comprehending test language and formats. Teachers can use specific strategies to prepare English language learners for assessment. Using these strategies on the Benchmark Tests will increase students' comfort levels and success with assessment tools such as the state tests.

Testing Strategies For All English Language Learners
Provide Accommodations for Students' Success

Any accommodations appropriate for English language learners should address students' linguistic needs, either directly or indirectly. As you consider accommodations for students taking the Benchmark Tests, remember that when the state tests are given, no special accommodations are allowed. Therefore, as you make accommodations for English language learners, keep in mind that the ultimate goal is for these students to handle mainstream testing settings, terminology, and instruction. Any accommodations that you provide should be considered stepping stones to students' eventual successful encounter with mainstream testing conditions.

1. **Simplify and clarify directions.** Providing instructions in simplified formats can reduce the language load for English language learners and help them focus solely on the task and content for the specific question(s). A good rule of thumb is to match the language used with the test to the language used with instruction. Students benefit from your replacing complex English words with simpler English words that they are already familiar with or can grasp more easily. However, it is never appropriate to translate test directions into students' home languages. This practice will not benefit students when they encounter state tests. (*See below* **A Word of Caution.**) However, you may ask students to restate directions in their own words so you are sure they understand them.

2. **Provide a setting consistent with the instructional setting.** Administering tests in an alternate, smaller, even one-on-one, setting can allow for verbal scaffolding and provide English language learners with a setting that is comfortable and familiar to them. Be sure that the alternate setting is a setting with which students are familiar. Move students to mainstream testing settings when you feel they are ready.

3. **Consider timing.** Provide additional testing time and allow frequent or extended breaks during testing. On the Benchmark Tests, for example, students may benefit from a break between the two Comprehension selection/item sets and after the Comprehension and Vocabulary sections before moving on to the Writing Conventions section. The Writing sections are rigorous for students. Consider completing these portions on a different day or after a significant break. Keep in mind, however, that while this type of accommodation is one that is most often used for English language learners in mainstream classrooms, it is more important to be sure that students are receiving the necessary linguistic support in English.

4. **Provide dictionaries.** Allow the use of bilingual, word-for-word translation dictionaries as an accommodation for students who are able to use them effectively.

A Word of Caution: In providing accommodations to students, it is important not to compromise the intent of the assessment. It is never appropriate to translate into students' native languages or read aloud in English selections and questions. These practices alter the constructs of the assessments. The reading comprehension assessments, for example, are designed to measure both word recognition and understanding, so translating or reading the selections to students actually changes the intent of the tests.

Following the administration of the assessments, it is important to note which accommodations were used for English language learners and to interpret scores with that information in mind. As students progress in their English language skills and become more comfortable with testing, it is important to reconsider accommodations that were provided on previous tests.

Familiarize Students with Academic Language and Test Language

The Benchmark Tests use routine terminology and formats that are designed to mirror the experience of taking state tests. Helping students improve their understanding and use of academic language is an essential way to prepare students for assessment. The practice of "teaching to the test" is often criticized—and rightfully so—but helping English language learners understand the language and formats of tests and other assessment instruments levels the playing field for these students, allowing them to demonstrate what they've learned about the content, rather than struggling with the test language and formats. All students, but especially English language learners, must be taught test-taking strategies and must build background about the language and procedures of taking tests. **What strategies can you explicitly offer to students to prepare for assessment?**

1. Focus on Academic English and Meaningful Oral Language Experiences
Many English language learners may quickly master *social* English, the conversational language skills and conventions used in everyday interactions with classmates. These same learners, however, frequently encounter difficulty with the *academic* English found on formal assessments. Students may also have gaps in understanding between oral and written English. The structure of academic English is complex, e.g., fiction and nonfiction text structures, paragraph organization, and syntax, including prepositional phrases, introductory clauses, and pronoun references. There are structural analysis constraints at the word, sentence, paragraph, and text levels.

Development of academic language is one of the primary sources of difficulty for English language learners at all ages and grades while also being fundamental to all students' success. The vocabulary of academic English consists of specialized meanings of common words, abstract concepts, multiple-meaning words, and words based on Latin and Greek roots. As students read test selections, they may encounter unfamiliar topics and concepts. Recognize that it takes years for students to master academic English, but that you can help them make progress on the way. Highlight and discuss routinely the *academic* language, vocabulary, syntax, and narrative and expository text structures encountered in textbooks and trade books. Remember that academic English is not another name for "standard English." Academic English is the special form of English that is used in the classroom and in written texts. The grammatical constructions, words, and rhetorical conventions are not often used in everyday spoken language. The home language does *not* have to be English in order for students to benefit from experiences in using academic language. If it proves helpful, students may be encouraged to connect what they know in their home languages to what they are learning about academic English.

Provide students with experiences with academic language by reading to them and discussing readings, instructional activities, and experiences. Draw students into instructional conversations focused on the language they encounter in their school texts and other materials to show students how language works. Provide students with ample opportunities to use the language of texts—and tests—in speaking and in writing. Provide regular opportunities for meaningful oral language experiences in which English language learners participate in discussion of important topics and perform the activities required on tests, such as explaining, describing, comparing, and stating and supporting opinions. Encourage them to use vocabulary that will support academic language development in increased opportunities for structured academic talk.

2. Focus on Test Directions

Help students understand phrases such as "make heavy dark marks" and "fill the circle completely" that are often used in test directions. When possible, model tasks and provide verbal directions in simpler, more common English words. Be explicit in your teaching, using the following examples as a guide.

- **Make heavy dark marks that fill the circle completely.**

- **If you erase a grid circle, do not redraw it.**

- **Do not make any stray marks on this answer sheet.**

For the directions above, talk about the word *heavy* and its different meanings. Be sure students understand that here it means "dark." Explain that a *grid circle* is simply a "circle," *redraw* means "draw again," and *stray marks* means "marks in other places." Model and gesture how to follow the directions: *I use this answer sheet, or page. I find the number of the question in the booklet, or book, and I match the number in the booklet to the number on the sheet, or page, like this. Then I find the circle for the letter of the correct answer and make it all dark, or black, with my pencil. I do not make other marks on the page.* Be sure students can fill in the test form clearly and neatly.

For the directions above, talk about the phrase *correctly completes*. Be sure that students understand that for fill-in-the-blank sentences they must "pick the word that makes the sentence sound correct," or "choose the word that makes sense in the sentence." Model how to follow the directions.

3. Focus on Terminology and Strategies

Think about terms that will make the most sense to students as you teach. Instead of using the words *directions, test,* and *fill,* for example, you might use common cognates such as *instructions, exam,* and *mark,* which translate to most Romance languages (i.e., in Spanish: *instrucciones, examen,* and *marca*). However, move students to the original test words as soon as possible.

Pre-teach the "language of tests" encountered in directions and test items, including:

Question words, such as: *who, what, which, where, when, why, how,* and *what kind*

Emphasis words, such as: *best, better, first, last, not, except, probably, major, main, mainly, both, neither, either, same, different, begin, end, most, mostly,* and *least*

Action words, such as: *explain, describe, compare,* and *discuss.*

Words such as *both* and *not* may seem simple, but their uses in test questions often prove otherwise. English language learners need help in seeing how such words frame and constrain ideas expressed in sentences in which they appear.

Throughout the year, students need robust vocabulary instruction in English for additional common test words and phrases such as *test form, test booklet, answer sheet, mark the space, best describes, author, reader, purpose, paragraph, selection, article, passage, research, composition, writing prompt, details, events, results, according to, alike, opposite of, statements of fact and opinion, include, present in, represent, base your answer on,* and *support your answer.* Examine the tests for other words and phrases that are important for students to learn.

Familiarize students with basic test formats such as the lettering of multiple-choice options, underlining of words, cloze sentences, and writing-prompt boxes, so that they develop skills in locating key information. Use released tests or models of tests, providing students with plenty of practice in test formats. Be explicit in your instruction, using the following examples as a guide.

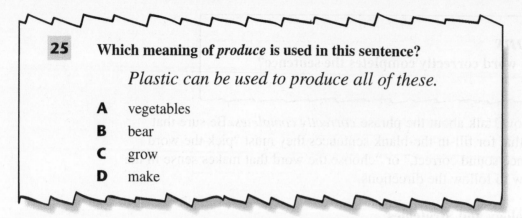

25   **Which meaning of *produce* is used in this sentence?**

Plastic can be used to produce all of these.

A   vegetables

B   bear

C   grow

D   make

Explain the test format: *Sometimes, test questions have words that are italicized. That means they look slanted. So the words should stand out; the print looks different from other words in the question. I pay special attention to those words. Questions ask about these words. This question asks about the meaning of the word.*

Use this entry from a dictionary to answer Number 26.

> **bank** \bangk\ *n* **1.** a piled up mass **2.** a place where money is kept **3.** the tilt of a turning vehicle **4.** the slope of land next to water

26   **What is the dictionary meaning for *bank* as used in this sentence?**

They steered into the bank underneath Lopa and Daka and started taking things from the canoes.

A   Definition 1

B   Definition 2

C   Definition 3

D   Definition 4

Explain the test format: *Some test questions use a dictionary entry, or the definitions or meanings of a word, to ask me what a word in the selection means. The word is italicized in the question. Some words have different meanings. The numbers in the dictionary entry show the different meanings of the word. I need to choose the right meaning. The correct answer is the meaning of the word as it is used in the sentence taken from the selection.* Model how to complete this type of question.

> ## PROMPT
>
> **You may have heard someone say that "experience is the best teacher." Think about a time when you learned some information or a new skill through experience. Write a story about what you learned and how you learned it.**

Explain the test format: *Some tests ask me to write a composition or story. At the top of the page is an instruction box, or writing prompt. First I read the instructions in the box to learn what to write about. The next two pages have lines for me to write on.* Explain also the "Checklist for Writers" box (see Unit 4 test, p. 16): *These are questions I read to myself and answer as I check over my writing to make sure it's just the way I want it.*

Model test-taking strategies for students. Help them use their emerging familiarity with vocabulary and basic language structures in English to select the best answer and eliminate multiple-choice options. Teach students the logic of test questions. Show students, for example, that the question "Which of the following is *not* a sentence?" entails that all of the listed options except one *are* sentences. Be sure to teach students the types of reading comprehension questions they may encounter on tests. Use released test items or models of test items to provide students with plenty of practice in question types and the test-taking strategies you have taught them. Be explicit in your instruction, using the following examples as a guide.

> **5**   **What happens in the <u>second stage</u> of <u>complete metamorphosis</u>?**
>
>   **A**   The egg hatches.
>   **B**   The insect grows wings.
>   **C**   The pupa forms a cocoon.
>   **D**   The larva eats and grows.

Model a test-taking strategy for students—underlining key words in the question: *I read the whole selection carefully before I try to answer the questions. What if I can't remember something? Do I guess? No. I can make lines under the important words in the question. Then I can search for these words in the selection. I can read that part of the selection again. This will help me find the correct answer.*

9 **Which sentence from the article is a statement of opinion?**

A A butterfly starts out as a tiny egg.

B They are little caterpillars in the larva stage, munching on leaves.

C The pupa stage is the most interesting stage of metamorphosis.

D When a frog hatches from its egg, it is a tadpole.

Model a test-taking strategy for students—eliminating incorrect multiple-choice options. *I read the whole selection carefully before I try to answer the questions. This question asks about an opinion. What is the difference between a statement of fact and a statement of opinion? A statement of fact can be proven true or false. A statement of opinion shows what someone feels or thinks about something. Now I read the answer choices. I try to find three answers that are not correct; they are statements of facts, not opinions. I am not sure if the first answer is opinion or fact. What do I do? I look for feeling or belief words. What are they?* Good examples are "beautiful," "wonderful," "great," and "amazing." *Does the first answer have a feeling or belief word? No, it is a statement of fact about butterfly eggs, so I do not choose this answer.* Continue to model eliminating incorrect multiple-choice options. *The third answer is the correct answer. It has the feeling or belief words "most interesting." That shows the author's opinion, or what she feels and thinks about metamorphosis.*

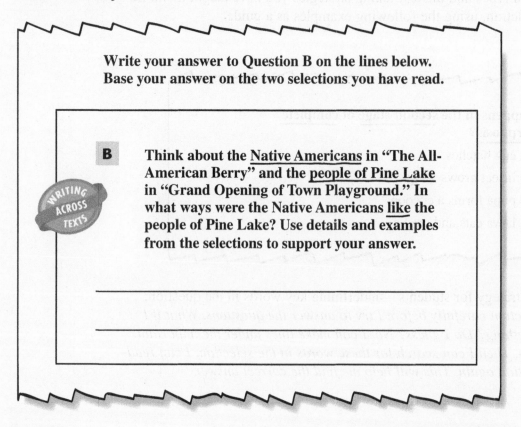

Write your answer to Question B on the lines below.
Base your answer on the two selections you have read.

B Think about the <u>Native Americans</u> in "The All-American Berry" and the <u>people of Pine Lake</u> in "Grand Opening of Town Playground." In what ways were the Native Americans <u>like</u> the people of Pine Lake? Use details and examples from the selections to support your answer.

_____

_____

Explain how to prepare for a constructed-response question: *I read both selections carefully before I try to answer this question. In this part of the test, I have to write. I read the question in the box to look for words that help me. I underline the important words—*Native Americans, people of Pine Lake, like. *The question says to "use details and examples from the selections." That means I need to think and write about both selections. What does "support my answer" mean? So, I must use information from both selections to show how the Native Americans and the people of Pine Lake were alike, or the same. I can search in the selections for the important words from the question. Then I can read carefully parts of the selections again to help me.*

Model for students how to read the test itself. Proficient English readers may benefit from strategies such as reading the test question and answer options first and then skimming the selection to find information that will help them select the correct answer to the question. English language learners are not served well by this option. They need to read and understand the selection carefully and then consider how to answer the questions asked. Model this type of test-taking strategy for students as you think aloud and explain the process.

Summarize test formats and strategies for students. Consider making a T-chart to show examples of the question types that students may find on tests. If your T-chart is large enough to be a wall chart, include examples of each type of item from released tests and model tests on the chart. Explain what the structures are and what they ask test-takers to do (or ask students to explain as you teach various strategies).

Evaluation Chart: Grade 4 — Unit 1 Benchmark Test

Student Name _____ Date _____

Reading – Parts 1–3

Item	Tested Skill	Item Type*	Common Core State Standard	Score (circle one)
Reading – Part 1: Comprehension				
1.	Author's purpose	C	Literature 1.	0 1
2.	Compare and contrast	I	Literature 1.	0 1
3.	Draw conclusions	C	Literature 1.	0 1
4.	Sequence	L	Literature 3.	0 1
5.	Draw conclusions	I	Literature 1.	0 1
6.	Draw conclusions	I	Literature 1.	0 1
7.	Literary elements: character	I	Literature 3.	0 1
8.	Sequence	L	Literature 3.	0 1
9.	Draw conclusions	I	Literature 1.	0 1
10.	Main idea and details	C	Literature 2.	0 1
11.	Sequence	C	Literature 1.	0 1
A.	Constructed-response text-to-self connection		Writing 1.	0 1 2
12.	Main idea and details	I	Informational Text 2.	0 1
13.	Main idea and details	I	Informational Text 2.	0 1
14.	Fact and opinion	C	Informational Text 1.	0 1
15.	Author's purpose	C	Informational Text 8.	0 1
16.	Author's purpose	C	Informational Text 8.	0 1
17.	Author's purpose	C	Informational Text 8.	0 1
18.	Main idea and details	L	Informational Text 2.	0 1
19.	Compare and contrast	I	Informational Text 1.	0 1
20.	Compare and contrast	L	Informational Text 1.	0 1
21.	Author's purpose	C	Informational Text 8.	0 1
22.	Draw conclusions	C	Informational Text 1.	0 1
B.	Constructed-response text-to-text connection		Writing 2.	0 1 2
Reading – Part 2: Vocabulary				
23.	Word structure: suffixes		Foundational Skills 3.a.	0 1
24.	Context clues: synonyms		Language 4.a.	0 1
25.	Word structure: suffixes		Foundational Skills 3.a.	0 1
26.	Context clues: unfamiliar words		Language 4.a.	0 1
27.	Word structure: suffixes		Language 4.a.	0 1
28.	Word structure: suffixes		Foundational Skills 3.a.	0 1
29.	Context clues: multiple-meaning words		Language 4.a.	0 1

	Reading – Part 2: Vocabulary (continued)				
30.	Context clues: synonyms	Language 4.a.	0	1	
31.	Context clues: multiple-meaning words	Language 4.a.	0	1	
32.	Word structure: suffixes	Foundational Skills 3.a.	0	1	

Reading – Part 3: Writing Conventions

33.	Imperative and exclamatory sentences	Language 1.	0	1	
34.	Declarative and interrogative sentences	Language 1.	0	1	
35.	Clauses and complex sentences	Language 1.	0	1	
36.	Clauses and complex sentences	Language 1.	0	1	
37.	Compound sentences	Language 1.	0	1	
38.	Clauses and complex sentences	Language 1.	0	1	
39.	Complete subjects and predicates	Language 1.	0	1	
40.	Complete subjects and predicates	Language 1.	0	1	

Student's Reading Total Score/Total Possible Score _____/44

*L = literal   I = inferential   C = critical analysis

Reading — Parts 1–3 percentage score: _____ ÷ 44 = _____ × 100 = _____%

(student's total score)   (percentage score)

Writing – Part 4

Writing Score (Complete one.) ____/6 ____/5 ____/4 ____/3	Common Core State Standards
Notes/Observations:	Writing 3. Writing 4. Language 1. Language 2.

Evaluation Chart: Grade 4 — Unit 2 Benchmark Test

Student Name _____ Date _____

Reading – Parts 1–3

Item	Tested Skill	Item Type*	Common Core State Standard	Score (circle one)
Reading – Part 1: Comprehension				
1.	Main idea and details	I	Informational Text 2.	0 1
2.	Main idea and details	I	Informational Text 2.	0 1
3.	Draw conclusions	I	Informational Text 1.	0 1
4.	Fact and opinion	C	Informational Text 1.	0 1
5.	Sequence	L	Informational Text 3.	0 1
6.	Sequence	L	Informational Text 3.	0 1
7.	Author's purpose	C	Informational Text 8.	0 1
8.	Draw conclusions	I	Informational Text 1.	0 1
9.	Draw conclusions	C	Informational Text 1.	0 1
10.	Author's purpose	C	Informational Text 8.	0 1
11.	Draw conclusions	I	Informational Text 1.	0 1
A.	Constructed-response text-to-world connection		Writing 2.	0 1 2
12.	Main idea and details	I	Informational Text 2.	0 1
13.	Draw conclusions	C	Informational Text 1.	0 1
14.	Sequence	L	Informational Text 3.	0 1
15.	Main idea and details	L	Informational Text 2.	0 1
16.	Main idea and details	L	Informational Text 2.	0 1
17.	Draw conclusions	C	Informational Text 1.	0 1
18.	Generalize	C	Informational Text 1.	0 1
19.	Main idea and details	I	Informational Text 2.	0 1
20.	Main idea and details	C	Informational Text 2.	0 1
21.	Main idea and details	I	Informational Text 2.	0 1
22.	Cause and effect	I	Informational Text 1.	0 1
B.	Constructed-response text-to-text connection		Writing 2.	0 1 2
Reading – Part 2: Vocabulary				
23.	Context clues: unfamiliar words		Language 4.a.	0 1
24.	Context clues: synonyms		Language 4.a.	0 1
25.	Word structure: suffixes		Foundational Skills 3.a.	0 1
26.	Word structure: suffixes		Language 4.a.	0 1
27.	Context clues: unfamiliar words		Language 4.a.	0 1
28.	Word structure: prefixes		Language 4.a.	0 1
29.	Word structure: suffixes		Foundational Skills 3.a.	0 1

- -

Reading – Part 2: Vocabulary (continued)			
30.	Word structure: suffixes	Language 4.a.	0 1
31.	Context clues: unfamiliar words	Language 4.a.	0 1
32.	Word structure: prefixes	Language 4.a.	0 1
Student's Regrouping Multiple-Choice Score/Total Response Score _____/32			
Reading – Part 3: Writing Conventions			
33.	Regular plural nouns	Language 1.	0 1
34.	Common and proper nouns	Language 1.	0 1
35.	Irregular plural nouns	Language 1.	0 1
36.	Regular plural nouns	Language 1.	0 1
37.	Irregular plural nouns	Language 1.	0 1
38.	Common and proper nouns	Language 1.	0 1
39.	Singular possessive nouns	Language 2.	0 1
40.	Plural possessive nouns	Language 2.	0 1
Student's Reading Total Score/Total Possible Score _____/44			

*L = literal   I = inferential   C = critical analysis

Regrouping (Reading — Parts 1–2) percentage score: _____ ÷ 32 = _____ × 100 = _____%

(student's score)   (percentage score)

Reading — Parts 1–3 percentage score: _____ ÷ 44 = _____ × 100 = _____%

(student's total score)   (percentage score)

Writing – Part 4		
Writing Score (Complete one.) _____/6 _____/5 _____/4 _____/3		**Common Core State Standards**
Notes/Observations:		Writing 2. Writing 4. Language 1. Language 2.

Evaluation Chart: Grade 4 — Unit 3 Benchmark Test

Student Name _____ Date _____

Reading – Parts 1–3

Item	Tested Skill	Item Type*	Common Core State Standard	Score (circle one)
Reading – Part 1: Comprehension				
1.	Author's purpose	I	Informational Text 8.	0 1
2.	Fact and opinion	C	Informational Text 1.	0 1
3.	Author's purpose	C	Informational Text 8.	0 1
4.	Main idea and details	C	Informational Text 2.	0 1
5.	Generalize	I	Informational Text 1.	0 1
6.	Fact and opinion	I	Informational Text 1.	0 1
7.	Draw conclusions	I	Informational Text 1.	0 1
8.	Author's purpose	C	Informational Text 2.	0 1
9.	Draw conclusions	I	Informational Text 1.	0 1
10.	Main idea and details	I	Informational Text 2.	0 1
11.	Draw conclusions	I	Informational Text 1.	0 1
A.	Constructed-response text-to-self connection		Writing 1.	0 1 2
12.	Literary elements: character	I	Informational Text 1.	0 1
13.	Fact and opinion	I	Informational Text 1.	0 1
14.	Cause and effect	L	Informational Text 8.	0 1
15.	Generalize	I	Informational Text 1.	0 1
16.	Draw conclusions	I	Informational Text 3.	0 1
17.	Author's purpose	I	Informational Text 2.	0 1
18.	Generalize	I	Informational Text 3.	0 1
19.	Cause and effect	I	Informational Text 3.	0 1
20.	Main idea and details	C	Informational Text 3.	0 1
21.	Generalize	I	Informational Text 3.	0 1
22.	Generalize	C	Informational Text 3.	0 1
B.	Constructed-response text-to-text connection		Writing 2.	0 1 2
Reading – Part 2: Vocabulary				
23.	Context clues: homonyms		Foundational Skills 3.	0 1
24.	Context clues: homonyms		Foundational Skills 3.	0 1
25.	Context clues: unfamiliar words		Language 4.a.	0 1
26.	Context clues: unfamiliar words		Language 4.a.	0 1
27.	Word structure: suffixes		Foundational Skills 3.a.	0 1
28.	Context clues: unfamiliar words		Language 4.a.	0 1
29.	Context clues: multiple-meaning words		Language 4.a.	0 1

Reading – Part 2: Vocabulary (continued)			
30.	Word structure: prefixes	Language 4.	0 1
31.	Context clues: unfamiliar words	Language 4.a.	0 1
32.	Context clues: multiple-meaning words	Language 4.	0 1
Student's Regrouping Multiple-Choice Score/Total Possible Score _____ /32			

Reading – Part 3: Writing Conventions			
33.	Past, present, and future verb tenses	Language 1.	0 1
34.	Past, present, and future verb tenses	Language 1.	0 1
35.	Action and linking verbs	Language 1.b.	0 1
36.	Past, present, and future verb tenses	Language 1.	0 1
37.	Past, present, and future verb tenses	Language 1.	0 1
38.	Main and helping verbs	Language 1.	0 1
39.	Past, present, and future verb tenses	Language 1.	0 1
40.	Subject-verb agreement	Language 1.	0 1
Student's Reading Total Score/Total Possible Score _____ /44			

*L = literal   I = inferential   C = critical analysis

Regrouping (Reading — Parts 1–2) percentage score: _____ ÷ 32 = _____ × 100 = _____%

                                                (student's score)   (percentage score)

Reading — Parts 1–3 percentage score: _____ ÷ 44 = _____ × 100 = _____%

                                      (student's total score)   (percentage score)

Writing – Part 4	**Common Core State Standards**
Writing Score (Complete one.) _____ /6 _____ /5 _____ /4 _____ /3	
Notes/Observations:	Writing 2. Writing 4. Language 1. Language 2.

Evaluation Chart: Grade 4 — Unit 4 Benchmark Test

Student Name _____ Date _____

Reading – Parts 1–3

Item	Tested Skill	Item Type*	Common Core State Standard	Score (circle one)
Reading – Part 1: Comprehension				
1.	Compare and contrast	I	Informational Text 3.	0 1
2.	Compare and contrast	L	Informational Text 3.	0 1
3.	Main idea and details	I	Informational Text 2.	0 1
4.	Cause and effect	I	Informational Text 1.	0 1
5.	Draw conclusions	I	Informational Text 3.	0 1
6.	Compare and contrast	L	Informational Text 3.	0 1
7.	Compare and contrast	L	Informational Text 3.	0 1
8.	Draw conclusions	C	Informational Text 1.	0 1
9.	Author's purpose	C	Informational Text 8.	0 1
10.	Main idea and details	C	Informational Text 2.	0 1
11.	Cause and effect	I	Informational Text 1.	0 1
A.	Constructed-response text-to-world connection		Writing 1.	0 1 2
12.	Literary elements: plot	C	Literature 1.	0 1
13.	Literary elements: character	C	Literature 3.	0 1
14.	Compare and contrast	I	Literature 3.	0 1
15.	Draw conclusions	I	Literature 1.	0 1
16.	Cause and effect	I	Literature 1.	0 1
17.	Draw conclusions	I	Literature 1.	0 1
18.	Draw conclusions	C	Literature 1.	0 1
19.	Compare and contrast	I	Literature 3.	0 1
20.	Cause and effect	I	Literature 3.	0 1
21.	Author's purpose	C	Literature 4.	0 1
22.	Cause and effect	I	Literature 3.	0 1
B.	Constructed-response text-to-text connection		Writing 2.	0 1 2
Reading – Part 2: Vocabulary				
23.	Context clues: synonyms		Language 4.a.	0 1
24.	Context clues: synonyms		Language 4.a.	0 1
25.	Context clues: antonyms		Language 4.	0 1
26.	Context clues: multiple-meaning words		Language 4.a.	0 1
27.	Context clues: antonyms		Language 4.	0 1
28.	Context clues: antonyms		Language 4.	0 1
29.	Context clues: unknown words		Language 4.a.	0 1

Reading – Part 2: Vocabulary (continued)			
30.	Context clues: antonyms	Language 4.	0 1
31.	Context clues: unknown words	Language 4.a.	0 1
32.	Context clues: multiple-meaning words	Language 4.a.	0 1
Student's Regrouping Multiple-Choice Score/Total Possible Score _____/32			
Reading – Part 3: Writing Conventions			
33.	Subject and object pronouns	Language 1.	0 1
34.	Pronouns and antecedents	Language 1.	0 1
35.	Subject and object pronouns	Language 1.	0 1
36.	Singular and plural pronouns	Language 1.	0 1
37.	Pronouns and antecedents	Language 1.	0 1
38.	Contractions and negatives	Language 2.	0 1
39.	Pronouns and antecedents	Language 1.	0 1
40.	Singular and plural pronouns	Language 1.	0 1
Student's Reading Total Score/Total Possible Score _____/44			

*L = literal   I = inferential   C = critical analysis

Regrouping (Reading — Parts 1–2) percentage score: _____ ÷ 32 = _____ × 100 = _____%

    (student's score)   (percentage score)

Reading — Parts 1–3 percentage score: _____ ÷ 44 = _____ × 100 = _____%

    (student's total score)   (percentage score)

Writing – Part 4	
Writing Score (Complete one.) ____/6 ____/5 ____/4 ____/3	**Common Core State Standards**
Notes/Observations:	Writing 3. Writing 4. Language 1. Language 2.

Evaluation Chart: Grade 4 — Unit 5 Benchmark Test

Student Name _____ Date _____

Reading – Parts 1–3

Item	Tested Skill	Item Type*	Common Core State Standard	Score (circle one)
Reading – Part 1: Comprehension				
1.	Sequence	I	Literature 3.	0 1
2.	Author's purpose	C	Literature 1.	0 1
3.	Literary elements: plot	I	Literature 3.	0 1
4.	Literary elements: character	C	Literature 3.	0 1
5.	Literary elements: character	C	Literature 3.	0 1
6.	Literary elements: theme	I	Literature 2.	0 1
7.	Draw conclusions	I	Literature 3.	0 1
8.	Literary elements: plot	I	Literature 3.	0 1
9.	Literary elements: theme	I	Literature 2.	0 1
10.	Literary elements: plot	I	Literature 3.	0 1
11.	Draw conclusions	I	Literature 1.	0 1
A.	Constructed-response text-to-world connection		Writing 2.	0 1 2
12.	Sequence	I	Informational Text 3.	0 1
13.	Author's purpose	C	Informational Text 8.	0 1
14.	Cause and effect	I	Informational Text 3.	0 1
15.	Main idea and details	I	Informational Text 2.	0 1
16.	Author's purpose	C	Informational Text 8.	0 1
17.	Fact and opinion	I	Informational Text 1.	0 1
18.	Cause and effect	I	Informational Text 3.	0 1
19.	Draw conclusions	I	Informational Text 1.	0 1
20.	Author's purpose	C	Informational Text 8.	0 1
21.	Main idea and details	C	Informational Text 2.	0 1
22.	Author's purpose	C	Informational Text 8.	0 1
B.	Constructed-response text-to-text connection		Writing 2.	0 1 2
Reading – Part 2: Vocabulary				
23.	Context clues: homographs		Language 4.a.	0 1
24.	Context clues: synonyms		Language 4.	0 1
25.	Context clues: synonyms		Language 4.	0 1
26.	Context clues: synonyms		Foundational Skills 3.	0 1
27.	Context clues: synonyms		Language 4.a.	0 1
28.	Context clues: homographs		Language 4.a.	0 1
29.	Context clues: synonyms		Language 4.	0 1

Reading – Part 2: Vocabulary (continued)

30.	Context clues: unfamiliar words	Language 4.a.	0 1
31.	Context clues: unfamiliar words	Language 4.a.	0 1
32.	Context clues: synonyms	Foundational Skills 3.	0 1
Student's Regrouping Multiple-Choice Score/Total Possible Score			**_____/32**

Reading – Part 3: Writing Conventions

33.	Adverbs	Language 1.	0 1
34.	Adjectives and articles	Language 1.	0 1
35.	Comparative and superlative adjectives	Language 1.	0 1
36.	Adverbs	Language 1.	0 1
37.	Adjectives	Language 1.	0 1
38.	Adverbs	Language 1.	0 1
39.	Prepositions	Language 1.e.	0 1
40.	Prepositions and prepositional phrases	Language 1.e.	0 1
Student's Reading Total Score/Total Possible Score			**_____/44**

*L = literal   I = inferential   C = critical analysis

Regrouping (Reading — Parts 1–2) percentage score: _____ ÷ 32 = _____ × 100 = _____%

(student's score)   (percentage score)

Reading – Parts 1–3 percentage score: _____ ÷ 44 = _____ × 100 = _____%

(student's total score)   (percentage score)

Writing – Part 4	Common Core State Standards
Writing Score (Complete one.) _____/6 _____/5 _____/4 _____/3	
Notes/Observations:	Writing 1. Writing 4. Language 1. Language 2.

Evaluation Chart: Grade 4 — Unit 6 Benchmark Test

Student Name _____ Date _____

Reading – Parts 1–3

Item	Tested Skill	Item Type*	Common Core State Standard	Score (circle one)
Reading – Part 1: Comprehension				
1.	Graphic sources	I	Informational Text 7.	0 1
2.	Fact and opinion	C	Informational Text 1.	0 1
3.	Graphic sources	I	Informational Text 7.	0 1
4.	Fact and opinion	C	Informational Text 1.	0 1
5.	Compare and contrast	L	Informational Text 1.	0 1
6.	Draw conclusions	I	Informational Text 3.	0 1
7.	Draw conclusions	I	Informational Text 3.	0 1
8.	Sequence	L	Informational Text 3.	0 1
9.	Main idea and details	C	Informational Text 2.	0 1
10.	Author's purpose	C	Informational Text 8.	0 1
11.	Cause and effect	L	Informational Text 3.	0 1
A.	Constructed-response text-to-world connection		Writing 1.	0 1 2
12.	Sequence	L	Informational Text 3.	0 1
13.	Draw conclusions	I	Informational Text 1.	0 1
14.	Main idea and details	I	Informational Text 2.	0 1
15.	Fact and opinion	C	Informational Text 1.	0 1
16.	Draw conclusions	I	Informational Text 1.	0 1
17.	Graphic sources	I	Informational Text 7.	0 1
18.	Author's purpose	C	Informational Text 8.	0 1
19.	Fact and opinion	I	Informational Text 1.	0 1
20.	Fact and opinion	C	Informational Text 1.	0 1
21.	Graphic sources	C	Informational Text 7.	0 1
22.	Graphic sources	I	Informational Text 7.	0 1
B.	Constructed-response text-to-text connection		Writing 2.	0 1 2
Reading – Part 2: Vocabulary				
23.	Word structure: root words		Language 4.	0 1
24.	Context clues: multiple-meaning words		Language 4.a.	0 1
25.	Word structure: root words		Language 4.	0 1
26.	Context clues: multiple-meaning words		Language 4.a.	0 1
27.	Context clues: multiple-meaning words		Language 4.a.	0 1
28.	Dictionary/glossary: unfamiliar words		Language 4.c.	0 1
29.	Dictionary/glossary: unfamiliar words		Language 4.c.	0 1

Reading – Part 2: Vocabulary (continued)			
30.	Dictionary/glossary: multiple-meaning words	Language 4.c.	0 1
31.	Dictionary/glossary: multiple-meaning words	Language 4.c.	0 1
32.	Dictionary/glossary: unfamiliar words	Language 4.c.	0 1
Student's Regrouping Multiple-Choice Score/Total Possible Score _____			/32
Reading – Part 3: Writing Conventions			
33.	Quotation marks	Language 2.b.	0 1
34.	Commas	Language 2.	0 1
35.	Capitalization	Language 2.a.	0 1
36.	Commas	Language 2.b.	0 1
37.	Quotation marks	Language 2.b.	0 1
38.	Conjunctions and combining sentences	Language 2.c.	0 1
39.	Conjunctions and combining sentences	Language 2.c.	0 1
40.	Capitalization	Language 2.a.	0 1
Student's Reading Total Score/Total Possible Score _____			/44

*L = literal   I = inferential   C = critical analysis

Regrouping (Reading — Parts 1–2) percentage score: _____ ÷ 32 = _____ × 100 = _____%

(student's score)   (percentage score)

Reading — Parts 1–3 percentage score: _____ ÷ 44 = _____ × 100 = _____%

(student's total score)   (percentage score)

Writing – Part 4	
Writing Score (Complete one.) _____/6 _____/5 _____/4 _____/3	**Common Core State Standards**
Notes/Observations:	Writing 3. Writing 4. Language 1. Language 2.

Evaluation Chart: Grade 4 — End-of-Year Benchmark Test

Student Name _____ Date _____

Reading – Parts 1–3

Item	Tested Skill	Item Type*	Common Core State Standard	Score (circle one)
Reading – Part 1: Comprehension				
1.	Compare and contrast	L	Informational Text 1.	0　1
2.	Compare and contrast	I	Informational Text 1.	0　1
3.	Graphic sources	I	Informational Text 7.	0　1
4.	Fact and opinion	C	Informational Text 1.	0　1
5.	Main idea and details	I	Informational Text 2.	0　1
6.	Author's purpose	C	Informational Text 8.	0　1
7.	Cause and effect	L	Informational Text 1.	0　1
8.	Sequence	I	Informational Text 3.	0　1
9.	Fact and opinion	C	Informational Text 1.	0　1
10.	Draw conclusions	C	Informational Text 1.	0　1
11.	Cause and effect	L	Informational Text 1.	0　1
12.	Cause and effect	L	Literature 1.	0　1
13.	Draw conclusions	I	Literature 1.	0　1
14.	Compare and contrast	I	Literature 3.	0　1
15.	Sequence	C	Literature 1.	0　1
16.	Author's purpose	C	Literature 1.	0　1
17.	Literary elements: theme	C	Literature 2.	0　1
18.	Literary elements: character	I	Literature 3.	0　1
19.	Main idea and details	I	Literature 2.	0　1
20.	Literary elements: plot	I	Literature 3.	0　1
21.	Literary elements: character	I	Literature 3.	0　1
22.	Sequence	I	Literature 3.	0　1
A.	Constructed-response text-to-text connection		Writing 2.	0　1　2
23.	Author's purpose	C	Informational Text 8.	0　1
24.	Sequence	I	Informational Text 1.	0　1
25.	Sequence	I	Informational Text 1.	0　1
26.	Cause and effect	I	Informational Text 5.	0　1
27.	Main idea and details	I	Informational Text 2.	0　1
28.	Draw conclusions	I	Informational Text 1.	0　1
29.	Main idea and details	C	Informational Text 2.	0　1
30.	Graphic sources	I	Informational Text 7.	0　1
31.	Graphic sources	I	Informational Text 7.	0　1
32.	Fact and opinion	C	Informational Text 1.	0　1
33.	Draw conclusions	I	Informational Text 1.	0　1
B.	Constructed-response text-to-text connection		Writing 2.	0　1　2

Reading – Part 2: Vocabulary

34.	Context clues: unfamiliar words	Language 4.a.	0 1
35.	Word structure: prefixes	Language 4.	0 1
36.	Context clues: multiple-meaning words	Language 4.a.	0 1
37.	Context clues: homonyms	Language 4.a.	0 1
38.	Context clues: unfamiliar words	Language 4.a.	0 1
39.	Context clues: antonyms	Language 4.	0 1
40.	Context clues: antonyms	Language 4.	0 1
41.	Context clues: unfamiliar words	Language 4.	0 1
42.	Word structure: suffixes	Foundational Skills 3.a.	0 1
43.	Context clues: synonyms	Language 4.	0 1
44.	Context clues: multiple-meaning words	Language 4.a.	0 1
45.	Context clues: multiple-meaning words	Language 4.a.	0 1
46.	Context clues: synonyms	Language 4.	0 1
47.	Dictionary: multiple-meaning words	Language 4.c.	0 1
48.	Dictionary: multiple-meaning words	Language 4.c.	0 1

Reading – Part 3: Writing Conventions

49.	Imperative and exclamatory sentences	Language 1.	0 1
50.	Adverbs	Language 1.	0 1
51.	Capitalization	Language 2.a.	0 1
52.	Compound and complex sentences	Language 1.f.	0 1
53.	Irregular plural nouns	Language 1.	0 1
54.	Possessive nouns	Language 1.	0 1
55.	Action and linking verbs	Language 1.	0 1
56.	Past, present, and future verb tenses	Language 1.	0 1
57.	Subject-verb agreement	Language 1.	0 1
58.	Pronouns and antecedents	Language 1.	0 1
59.	Comparative and superlative adjectives	Language 1.	0 1
60.	Commas	Language 2.	0 1
	Student's Reading Total Score/Total Possible Score	**_____/64**	

*L = literal   I = inferential   C = critical analysis

Reading — Parts 1–3 percentage score: _____ ÷ 64 = _____ × 100 = _____%

      (student's total score)   (percentage score)

Writing – Part 4		Common Core State Standards
Writing Score (Complete one.) _____/6 _____/5 _____/4 _____/3		
Notes/Observations:		Writing 1. Writing 4. Language 1. Language 2.

CLASS RECORD CHART
Grade 4 Unit Benchmark Tests

Teacher Name _____ Class _____

Student Name	Unit 1		Unit 2		Unit 3		Unit 4		Unit 5		Unit 6	
	Pt 1–3	Pt 4	Pt 1–3	Pt 4	Pt 1–3	Pt 4	Pt 1–3	Pt 4	Pt 1–3	Pt 4	Pt 1–3	Pt 4
1.												
2.												
3.												
4.												
5.												
6.												
7.												
8.												
9.												
10.												
11.												
12.												
13.												
14.												
15.												
16.												
17.												
18.												
19.												
20.												
21.												
22.												
23.												
24.												
25.												
26.												
27.												
28.												
29.												
30.												

■ ■ ■ CLASS RECORD CHART

Teacher Name _____   Class _____

Student Name	Unit 1			Unit 2			Unit 3			Unit 4			Unit 5			Unit 6	
	Pr 1–3	Pr 4	Pr 4	Pr 1–3	Pr 4	Pr 4	Pr 1–3	Pr 4	Pr 4	Pr 1–3	Pr 4	Pr 4	Pr 1–3	Pr 4	Pr 4	Pr 4
1.																
2.																
3.																
4.																
5.																
6.																
7.																
8.																
9.																
10.																
11.																
12.																
13.																
14.																
15.																
16.																
17.																
18.																
19.																
20.																
21.																
22.																
23.																
24.																
25.																
26.																
27.																
28.																
29.																
30.																

ANSWER KEYS

Unit 1 Benchmark Test

Reading – Part 1: Comprehension

Selection 1: "Let It Snow"

1. C
2. J
3. C
4. J
5. B
6. F
7. D
8. G
9. A
10. G
11. C

A. Use the Constructed-Response Scoring Rubric on page T11 to help you assess students' responses. Assign each response a score from 0 to 2.

A possible top response might be:

What I like best about snow is that I can make a snowman or a snow fort. I also like to go sledding in the snow. In addition, I like to watch snowflakes fall, and it's interesting to me that there are no two snowflakes alike.

Selection 2: "State License Plates"

12. H
13. D
14. F
15. C
16. J
17. B
18. G
19. A

20. F
21. D
22. G

B. Use the Constructed-Response Scoring Rubric on page T11 to help you assess students' responses. Assign each response a score from 0 to 2.

A possible top response might be:

Both selections provide information about states. The author wrote "Let It Snow" to entertain. The author of "State License Plates" was writing to inform readers about the variety of license plates states have.

Reading – Part 2: Vocabulary

23. D
24. H
25. D
26. J
27. C
28. H
29. A
30. J
31. B
32. F

Reading – Part 3: Writing Conventions

33. C
34. F
35. B
36. F
37. A

38. J

39. A

40. J

Writing – Part 4

Prompt: Students are to tell a story about when they planned a surprise for someone or when someone surprised them. Students are to describe how they felt.

Scoring: Use one of the Narrative Writing Scoring Rubrics on pages T12–T13 to help you assess students' compositions. Choose one of the four rubrics, and assign each composition a score based on the 6-point, 5-point, 4-point, or 3-point scale.

Unit 2 Benchmark Test

Reading – Part 1: Comprehension

Selection 1: "The All-American Berry"

1. D

2. J

3. C

4. F

5. B

6. H

7. B

8. F

9. C

10. G

11. D

A. Use the Constructed-Response Scoring Rubric on page T11 to help you assess students' responses. Assign each response a score from 0 to 2.

A possible top response might be:

You should read through the entire recipe so that you'll know if you have everything to cook with. You will also get an idea of how much time it will take and how much help you will need.

Selection 2: "Grand Opening of Town Playground"

12. J

13. A

14. J

15. D

16. H

17. B

18. J

19. C

20. F

21. D

22. G

B. Use the Constructed-Response Scoring Rubric on page T11 to help you assess students' responses. Assign each response a score from 0 to 2.

A possible top response might be:

They were both alike because they both shared their knowledge and talents. The Native Americans knew about blueberries and shared this information with the settlers. The people of Pine Lake shared their talents and labor to make the playground possible.

Reading – Part 2: Vocabulary

23. B

24. G

25. A

26. J

27. D

28. F

29. C

30. J

31. B

32. G

Reading – Part 3: Writing Conventions

33. C

34. H

35. D

36. G

37. A

38. H

39. B

40. G

Writing – Part 4

Prompt: Students are asked to explain something they know how to do.

Scoring: Use one of the Expository Writing Scoring Rubrics on pages T16–T17 to help you assess students' compositions. Choose one of the four rubrics, and assign each composition a score based on the 6-point, 5-point, 4-point, or 3-point scale.

Unit 3 Benchmark Test

Reading – Part 1: Comprehension

Selection 1: "Snowflakes"

1. C

2. J

3. A

4. G

5. B

6. H

7. A

8. J

9. C

10. F

11. C

A. Use the Constructed-Response Scoring Rubric on page T11 to help you assess students' responses. Assign each response a score from 0 to 2.

A possible top response might be:

Snowflakes are beautiful to me. I have looked at them with a magnifying glass, and I agree with the author that they are amazing pieces of art because each one is unique and pretty.

Selection 2: "Blending In"

12. H

13. B

14. F

15. B

16. H

17. C

18. J

19. C

20. F

21. B

22. F

B. Use the Constructed-Response Scoring Rubric on page T11 to help you assess students' responses. Assign each response a score from 0 to 2.

A possible top response might be:

If we look very closely at snowflakes, we can see that they are not exactly the same, like when you look closely at twins. If we look closely while we are in the woods, we may see animals that try to blend in by using camouflage.

Reading – Part 2: Vocabulary

23. A

24. J

25. A

26. H

27. D

28. J

29. A

30. G

31. B

32. G

Reading – Part 3: Writing Conventions

33. C

34. H

35. D

36. H

37. A

38. J

39. A

40. H

Writing – Part 4

Prompt: Students are asked to write an essay about seeing or understanding something in a new and different way. Students are to compare their understanding before and after seeing something in a new way.

Scoring: Use one of the Expository Writing Scoring Rubrics on pages T16–T17 to help you assess students' compositions. Choose one of the four rubrics, and assign each composition a score based on the 6-point, 5-point, 4-point, or 3-point scale.

Unit 4 Benchmark Test

Reading – Part 1: Comprehension

Selection 1: "Hawk Identification"

1. B

2. F

3. C

4. H

5. A

6. G

7. D

8. J

9. C

10. J

11. B

A. Use the Constructed-Response Scoring Rubric on page T11 to help you assess students' responses. Assign each response a score from 0 to 2.

A possible top response might be:

The person would need to like details and would need to be patient. The person should not be easily discouraged and should be determined enough to spend a lot of time in the field.

Selection 2: "The Hunt"

12. G

13. A

14. J

15. C

16. G

17. D

18. G

19. D

20. F

21. C

22. J

B. Use the Constructed-Response Scoring Rubric on page T11 to help you assess students' responses. Assign each response a score from 0 to 2.

A possible top response might be:

Both selections teach a lesson about watching carefully. In "Hawk Identification" the author teaches the things to look for in order to tell two kinds of hawks apart. In "The Hunt," the grandfather is teaching his grandson how to hunt by watching the animals closely.

Reading – Part 2: Vocabulary

23. D

24. F

25. C

26. J

27. B

28. J

29. A

30. J

31. D

32. H

Reading – Part 3: Writing Conventions

33. A

34. J

35. B

36. G

37. A

38. F

39. D

40. J

Writing – Part 4

Prompt: Students are asked to write a story describing a time when they learned something new through experience.

Scoring: Use one of the Narrative Writing Scoring Rubrics on pages T12–T13 to help you assess students' compositions. Choose one of the four rubrics, and assign each composition a score based on the 6-point, 5-point, 4-point, or 3-point scale.

Unit 5 Benchmark Test

Reading – Part 1: Comprehension

Selection 1: "A New Start"

1. B

2. H

3. D

4. G

5. C

6. H

7. D

8. J

9. A

10. F

11. D

A. Use the Constructed-Response Scoring Rubric on page T11 to help you assess students' responses. Assign each response a score from 0 to 2.

A possible top response might be:

People in my family help each other with jobs all the time, just as Sarah and her parents helped each other. We don't have hard jobs like building a house out of sod, but we clean the house and rake the leaves together. We try to help our neighbors, and we have made friends with our neighbors too, just as Sarah's family did. We all help each other in hard times, just as in the story.

Selection 2: "The Vine That Ate the South"

12. H

13. D

14. F

15. B

16. J

17. C

18. J

19. C

20. J

21. B

22. F

B. Use the Constructed-Response Scoring Rubric on page T11 to help you assess students' responses. Assign each response a score from 0 to 2.

A possible top response might be:

In both selections, people make use of the things that are found in their surroundings. For example, in "A New Start," Sarah's

family uses sod to make a house in a place where there is very little timber. In "The Vine That Ate the South," some people use kudzu to feed goats, and then they sell the goat's milk and wool.

Reading – Part 2: Vocabulary

23. A

24. H

25. D

26. H

27. B

28. H

29. D

30. F

31. B

32. J

Reading – Part 3: Writing Conventions

33. C

34. J

35. A

36. J

37. B

38. H

39. A

40. H

Writing – Part 4

Prompt: Students are asked to think about a problem to solve and write an essay that will convince their classmates that his or her solution to the problem will work.

Scoring: Use one of the Persuasive Writing Scoring Rubrics on pages T18–T19 to help you assess students' compositions. Choose one of the four rubrics, and assign each composition a score based on the 6-point, 5-point, 4-point, or 3-point scale.

Unit 6 Benchmark Test

Reading – Part 1: Comprehension

Selection 1: "From Trash to Treasure"

1. D
2. F
3. C
4. J
5. A
6. H
7. A
8. G
9. D
10. H
11. B

A. Use the Constructed-Response Scoring Rubric on page T11 to help you assess students' responses. Assign each response a score from 0 to 2.

A possible top response might be:

Recycling is good because things can be used again instead of being thrown in a landfill and taking up space. Plastic can be used to make all sorts of things, even clothes! That is good because plastic stays in landfills for 100 years or more.

Selection 2: "Harriet Tubman: Making a Difference"

12. H
13. A
14. J
15. A
16. H
17. B
18. J
19. D
20. H
21. B
22. G

B. Use the Constructed-Response Scoring Rubric on page T11 to help you assess students' responses. Assign each response a score from 0 to 2.

A possible top response might be:

"From Trash to Treasure" tells how plastic can be made into fleece. This makes things better because we save resources. "Harriet Tubman" is about how Tubman made things better for her family and others by helping them escape to freedom.

Reading – Part 2: Vocabulary

23. A
24. J
25. B
26. G
27. B
28. J
29. C
30. J
31. B
32. J

Reading – Part 3: Writing Conventions

33. B
34. J
35. C
36. F
37. D
38. F
39. D
40. G

Writing – Part 4

Prompt: Students are asked to write an essay describing a time they worked to make something better. They are to include a description of the thing they changed both before and after the change.

Scoring: Use one of the Descriptive Writing Scoring Rubrics on pages T14–T15 to help you assess students' compositions. Choose one of the four rubrics, and assign each composition a score based on the 6-point, 5-point, 4-point, or 3-point scale.

End-of-Year Benchmark Test

Reading – Part 1: Comprehension

Selection 1: "Sejong the Great"

1. A
2. H
3. B
4. J
5. C
6. H
7. A
8. G
9. B

10. J
11. B

Selection 2: "The Secret Code"

12. G
13. A
14. F
15. B
16. G
17. D
18. H
19. B
20. H
21. B
22. G

A. Use the Constructed-Response Scoring Rubric on page T11 to help you assess students' responses. Assign each response a score from 0 to 2.

A possible top response might be:

The selections both tell about people inventing new languages. However, one is true, and the other is not. "Sejong the Great" is a biography about a real king who invented a real language called hangul. "The Secret Code" is a fictional story about two kids who make up a language to write notes to each other.

Selection 3: "Going to Tiger Mountain"

23. C
24. F
25. B
26. J
27. D
28. G

29. C

30. J

31. C

32. F

33. C

B. Use the Constructed-Response Scoring Rubric on page T11 to help you assess students' responses. Assign each response a score from 0 to 2.

A possible top response might be:

The purpose of the notes in "The Secret Code" is to communicate in a fun way. Avi and Lydia are friends, and they write to each other to show they like each other. In "Going to Tiger Mountain," Ms. Ramírez writes the letter to tell students how to prepare for a field trip.

Reading – Part 2: Vocabulary

34. H

35. A

36. J

37. B

38. G

39. D

40. G

41. D

42. F

43. C

44. J

45. B

46. G

47. A

48. F

Reading – Part 3: Writing Conventions

49. B

50. F

51. B

52. H

53. C

54. F

55. A

56. J

57. C

58. H

59. D

60. F

Writing – Part 4

Prompt: Students are to write a persuasive essay to the principal giving reasons why starting an outdoors skills program at school would be a good or bad idea.

Scoring: Use one of the Persuasive Writing Scoring Rubrics on pages T18–T19 to help you assess students' compositions. Choose one of the four rubrics, and assign each composition a score based on the 6-point, 5-point, 4-point, or 3-point scale.

ANSWER SHEET

Unit Benchmark Tests

Student Name _____ Unit _____

Teacher Name _____ Date _____

Important Directions for Marking Answers

- Use black lead pencil (No. 2).
- Make heavy dark marks that fill the circle completely.
- Erase completely any answers you wish to change.
- If you erase a grid circle, do not redraw it.
- Do not make any stray marks on this answer sheet.

CORRECT MARK

Ⓐ ● Ⓒ Ⓓ

INCORRECT MARKS

Reading – Part 1: Comprehension

1. Ⓕ Ⓖ Ⓗ Ⓙ   6. Ⓐ Ⓑ Ⓒ Ⓓ   11. Ⓐ Ⓑ Ⓒ Ⓓ   16. Ⓕ Ⓖ Ⓗ Ⓙ   21. Ⓐ Ⓑ Ⓒ Ⓓ

2. Ⓐ Ⓑ Ⓒ Ⓓ   7. Ⓕ Ⓖ Ⓗ Ⓙ   12. Ⓕ Ⓖ Ⓗ Ⓙ   17. Ⓐ Ⓑ Ⓒ Ⓓ   22. Ⓕ Ⓖ Ⓗ Ⓙ

3. Ⓕ Ⓖ Ⓗ Ⓙ   8. Ⓐ Ⓑ Ⓒ Ⓓ   13. Ⓐ Ⓑ Ⓒ Ⓓ   18. Ⓕ Ⓖ Ⓗ Ⓙ

4. Ⓐ Ⓑ Ⓒ Ⓓ   9. Ⓕ Ⓖ Ⓗ Ⓙ   14. Ⓕ Ⓖ Ⓗ Ⓙ   19. Ⓐ Ⓑ Ⓒ Ⓓ

5. Ⓕ Ⓖ Ⓗ Ⓙ   10. Ⓐ Ⓑ Ⓒ Ⓓ   15. Ⓐ Ⓑ Ⓒ Ⓓ   20. Ⓕ Ⓖ Ⓗ Ⓙ

Reading – Part 2: Vocabulary

23. Ⓐ Ⓑ Ⓒ Ⓓ   25. Ⓐ Ⓑ Ⓒ Ⓓ   27. Ⓐ Ⓑ Ⓒ Ⓓ   29. Ⓐ Ⓑ Ⓒ Ⓓ   31. Ⓐ Ⓑ Ⓒ Ⓓ

24. Ⓕ Ⓖ Ⓗ Ⓙ   26. Ⓕ Ⓖ Ⓗ Ⓙ   28. Ⓕ Ⓖ Ⓗ Ⓙ   30. Ⓕ Ⓖ Ⓗ Ⓙ   32. Ⓕ Ⓖ Ⓗ Ⓙ

Reading – Part 3: Writing Conventions

33. Ⓐ Ⓑ Ⓒ Ⓓ   35. Ⓐ Ⓑ Ⓒ Ⓓ   37. Ⓐ Ⓑ Ⓒ Ⓓ   39. Ⓐ Ⓑ Ⓒ Ⓓ

34. Ⓕ Ⓖ Ⓗ Ⓙ   36. Ⓕ Ⓖ Ⓗ Ⓙ   38. Ⓕ Ⓖ Ⓗ Ⓙ   40. Ⓕ Ⓖ Ⓗ Ⓙ

ANSWER SHEET
End-of-Year Benchmark Test

Student Name _____ Date _____

Teacher Name _____

Important Directions for Marking Answers

- Use black lead pencil (No. 2).
- Make heavy dark marks that fill the circle completely.
- Erase completely any answers you wish to change.
- If you erase a grid circle, do not redraw it.
- Do not make any stray marks on this answer sheet.

CORRECT MARK

Ⓐ ● Ⓒ Ⓓ

INCORRECT MARKS

Ⓐ Ⓧ Ⓒ Ⓓ

Reading – Part 1: Comprehension

1. Ⓐ Ⓑ Ⓒ Ⓓ
2. Ⓕ Ⓖ Ⓗ Ⓙ
3. Ⓐ Ⓑ Ⓒ Ⓓ
4. Ⓕ Ⓖ Ⓗ Ⓙ
5. Ⓐ Ⓑ Ⓒ Ⓓ
6. Ⓕ Ⓖ Ⓗ Ⓙ
7. Ⓐ Ⓑ Ⓒ Ⓓ

8. Ⓕ Ⓖ Ⓗ Ⓙ
9. Ⓐ Ⓑ Ⓒ Ⓓ
10. Ⓕ Ⓖ Ⓗ Ⓙ
11. Ⓐ Ⓑ Ⓒ Ⓓ
12. Ⓕ Ⓖ Ⓗ Ⓙ
13. Ⓐ Ⓑ Ⓒ Ⓓ
14. Ⓕ Ⓖ Ⓗ Ⓙ

15. Ⓐ Ⓑ Ⓒ Ⓓ
16. Ⓕ Ⓖ Ⓗ Ⓙ
17. Ⓐ Ⓑ Ⓒ Ⓓ
18. Ⓕ Ⓖ Ⓗ Ⓙ
19. Ⓐ Ⓑ Ⓒ Ⓓ
20. Ⓕ Ⓖ Ⓗ Ⓙ
21. Ⓐ Ⓑ Ⓒ Ⓓ

22. Ⓕ Ⓖ Ⓗ Ⓙ
23. Ⓐ Ⓑ Ⓒ Ⓓ
24. Ⓕ Ⓖ Ⓗ Ⓙ
25. Ⓐ Ⓑ Ⓒ Ⓓ
26. Ⓕ Ⓖ Ⓗ Ⓙ
27. Ⓐ Ⓑ Ⓒ Ⓓ
28. Ⓕ Ⓖ Ⓗ Ⓙ

29. Ⓐ Ⓑ Ⓒ Ⓓ
30. Ⓕ Ⓖ Ⓗ Ⓙ
31. Ⓐ Ⓑ Ⓒ Ⓓ
32. Ⓕ Ⓖ Ⓗ Ⓙ
33. Ⓐ Ⓑ Ⓒ Ⓓ

Reading – Part 2: Vocabulary

34. Ⓕ Ⓖ Ⓗ Ⓙ
35. Ⓐ Ⓑ Ⓒ Ⓓ
36. Ⓕ Ⓖ Ⓗ Ⓙ

37. Ⓐ Ⓑ Ⓒ Ⓓ
38. Ⓕ Ⓖ Ⓗ Ⓙ
39. Ⓐ Ⓑ Ⓒ Ⓓ

40. Ⓕ Ⓖ Ⓗ Ⓙ
41. Ⓐ Ⓑ Ⓒ Ⓓ
42. Ⓕ Ⓖ Ⓗ Ⓙ

43. Ⓐ Ⓑ Ⓒ Ⓓ
44. Ⓕ Ⓖ Ⓗ Ⓙ
45. Ⓐ Ⓑ Ⓒ Ⓓ

46. Ⓕ Ⓖ Ⓗ Ⓙ
47. Ⓐ Ⓑ Ⓒ Ⓓ
48. Ⓕ Ⓖ Ⓗ Ⓙ

Reading – Part 3: Writing Conventions

49. Ⓐ Ⓑ Ⓒ Ⓓ
50. Ⓕ Ⓖ Ⓗ Ⓙ
51. Ⓐ Ⓑ Ⓒ Ⓓ

52. Ⓕ Ⓖ Ⓗ Ⓙ
53. Ⓐ Ⓑ Ⓒ Ⓓ
54. Ⓕ Ⓖ Ⓗ Ⓙ

55. Ⓐ Ⓑ Ⓒ Ⓓ
56. Ⓕ Ⓖ Ⓗ Ⓙ
57. Ⓐ Ⓑ Ⓒ Ⓓ

58. Ⓕ Ⓖ Ⓗ Ⓙ
59. Ⓐ Ⓑ Ⓒ Ⓓ
60. Ⓕ Ⓖ Ⓗ Ⓙ

OPTIONAL — FLUENCY CHECKS OR RUNNING RECORDS

How to Administer and Score a Fluency Test

A fluency test measures a student's reading rate, or the number of words correctly read per minute (wcpm), on grade-level text the student has not seen before. Give the student a copy of the Student Copy of the passage for the test and make a copy of the Teacher Copy for yourself, noting the formula for calculation at the bottom of the page. (The Teacher Copy has a scale of running numbers to make it easier for you to know how many words the student read during the fluency check, while the passage on the Student Copy does not have the numbers.) Make sure you have put the student's name and the test date at the top of your copy of the passage. Have a watch or clock with a second hand available for timing the reading.

Have the student read the text aloud. Do not have the student read the title as part of the fluency reading; it is not included in the running word count. (You may want to tape-record the student's reading for later evaluation.) Stop the student at exactly one minute and note precisely where the student stopped.

As the student reads orally, on your copy of the text, mark any miscues or errors the student makes during the reading (see the chart on page T58). Count the total number of words the student read in one minute. Subtract any words the student read incorrectly. Record the words correct per minute score on the test.

The formula is: Total # of words read – # of errors = words correct per minute (wcpm).

How to Identify Reading Miscues/Errors

Using the passage on page T59, the chart below shows the kinds of miscues and errors to look for as a student reads aloud and the notations to use to mark them.

Reading Miscue	Notations
Omission The student omits words or word parts.	You can whip up ⓐ batter in a matter of minutes.
Substitution The student substitutes words or parts of words for the words in the text.	First, mix a tablespoon of baking powder w̲i̲t̲h̲ *and* a half cup of flour.
Insertion The student inserts words or parts of words that are not in the text.	The name depends on where you live ᴧ *too*.
Mispronunciation/Misreading The student pronounces or reads a word incorrectly.	This all-American food is delicious *delicate* and easy to make.
Hesitation The student hesitates over a word and the teacher provides the word.	But they go by other names as well including g̲r̲i̲d̲d̲l̲e̲ cakes and hot cakes.
Self-correction The student reads a word incorrectly but then corrects the error.	Slowly mix the dry ingredients ⓈⒸ with the wet ones.

Notes

- If the student hesitates over a word, wait several seconds before telling the student what the word is.

- If a student makes the same error more than once, count it as only one error.

- Self-correction is not counted as an actual error. However, writing "SC" over the word or words will help you identify words that give the student some difficulty.

Sample Fluency Test

Here is the passage marked as shown on the chart on the previous page. As the student reads the passage aloud to you, mark miscues and errors. Have the student read for exactly one minute, and then mark the last word the student reads.

Student Name *Susan*   Date *9/7/2009*

Flapjacks (107)

You may know them as flapjacks. But they go by other names as well, including	15
H griddle cakes and hot cakes. The name depends on where you live. Still, most ^{too}	29
Americans know a pancake when they see one.	37
This all-American food is delicious and easy to make. You can whip up a batter *delicate*	52
in a matter of minutes. All you need is milk, an egg, butter, flour, baking powder,	68
and oil.	70
First, mix a tablespoon of baking powder ~~with~~ *and* a half cup of flour. Next, beat	85
together the egg with a half cup of milk and a quarter cup of oil. Slowly mix the dry	104
(SC) ingredients with the wet ones.	109
Now your batter is ready. Heat up a large frying pan and add two tablespoons	124
of butter. Pour spoonfuls of batter into the melted butter. Let the pancakes fry until	139
they are golden brown on the bottom. Flip them over and brown them on the other	155
side. Serve the pancakes hot with maple syrup, honey, or jam.	166

112 – 5 = 107

Interpreting the Results

According to published norms for oral reading fluency, students at the end of Grade 4 should be reading fluently at 130 words correct per minute in text that is on grade level. This chart gives recommended progress toward that goal.

End of Unit/Grade		Reading Rate (wcpm)
Grade 4	Unit 1	95 to 105
Grade 4	Unit 2	100 to 110
Grade 4	Unit 3	105 to 115
Grade 4	Unit 4	110 to 120
Grade 4	Unit 5	115 to 125
Grade 4	Unit 6	120 to 130
End-of-Year Goal		130

If a student's reading rate is lower than the suggested progress toward the standard for his or her grade level, your notes on the student's miscues may help you determine why the rate is low. Does the student make errors that indicate his or her decoding skills are poor? If so, further instruction in phonics may be needed. Do the errors reflect a lack of comprehension or limited vocabulary? In that case, instruction in comprehension strategies and exposure to more vocabulary words may help. A lack of fluency may indicate a lack of exposure to models of fluent oral reading. It may also mean that the student isn't reading enough material at his or her reading level.

How to Take a Running Record

A Running Record is an assessment of oral reading accuracy and oral reading fluency. A student's reading accuracy is based on the number of words read correctly. This measure is determined by an analysis of the errors a student makes—a miscue analysis. Reading fluency is based on reading rate (the number of words read per minute) and the degree to which the student reads with a "natural flow."

A Running Record may be taken using any reading passage at any time. However, the most valid and reliable assessment fulfills these requirements: (1) the text is appropriate to the student's reading level and interest, and (2) the text is unfamiliar to the student. The passages in this section are well suited for use as either a Fluency Test or with a Running Record because they fit these requirements. For additional oral reading accuracy and fluency checks that involve a Running Record, you may choose other passages from grade-level appropriate texts.

The Running Record may be used to verify instructional decisions suggested by other assessments, such as a Placement or Benchmark Test. It may also be used to identify a student's particular strengths and weaknesses in reading and language development. In addition, the Running Record may be administered periodically throughout the year as a means of monitoring student progress.

Measuring oral reading accuracy and oral reading fluency may be accomplished in a single reading, but two different operations are required. The guidelines on pages T62 and T63 explain how to determine each measurement.

How to Measure Oral Reading Accuracy

1. Choose an appropriate grade-level text of about 100 to 200 words, or use those passages that have been provided, for use as a Fluency Test.

2. Make copies of the text—one of the Student Copy for the student and one of the Teacher Copy for you. If the text appears in a book, you may have the student read the text from the book.

3. Give the text to the student and have the student read the text aloud. (You may want to tape-record the student's reading for later evaluation. This approach can be especially helpful if you are timing the student's reading or conducting other assessments at the same time.)

4. Your hand should always be "running" on your copy of the text. Put a checkmark above every word the student reads correctly. Mark any miscues or errors the student makes during the reading (see the explanation of reading miscues/errors for Fluency Tests beginning on page T58).

5. Count the total number of errors the student makes and find the percentage score for the number of errors. If you are using a fluency/running record passage from this book, the total word count is indicated for each passage, and a formula for determining a percentage score is provided.

6. If you are using a text from a different source, use this formula to get a percentage score:

$$\frac{\text{Total \# of words minus \# of errors}}{\text{Total \# of words}} \times 100 = \text{percentage score}$$

Example: Suppose a student reads a text of 110 words and makes 6 errors.

$$\frac{110 - 6 = 104 \text{ words}}{110} = 0.945 \qquad 0.945 \times 100 = 94.5\% \text{ (round to 95\%)}$$

The percentage score indicates the student's oral reading accuracy (percentage of words in the passage read correctly).

Benchmark Test Teacher's Manual

How to Measure Reading Rate

Reading rate is generally defined as number of words per minute (wpm). To determine the reading rate, follow steps 1–3 as described on page T62. Note the exact time when the student begins reading and the time when he or she finishes.

To calculate the number of words per minute, use the formula below:

$$\frac{\text{Total \# of words read}}{\text{\# of seconds}} \times 60 = \text{words per minute}$$

Example: Suppose a student reads a passage of 120 words in 90 seconds.

$$\frac{120}{90} = 1.33 \text{ (round to the nearest hundredth)}$$

$1.33 \times 60 = 79.8$ words per minute (round to 80 wpm)

Interpreting the Results

For oral reading accuracy, use the following criteria:

- A student who reads 98%–100% of the words correctly is reading at an independent level and may need more challenging texts.

- A student who reads 91%–97% of the words correctly is reading at an instructional level and will likely benefit from guided on-level instruction in the regular program.

- A student who reads with an accuracy of 90% or less is reading at a frustration level and may benefit most from targeted instruction with lower-level texts or strategic intervention.

For any student whose Running Record results are not clearly definitive, we recommend administering additional individual assessments, such as classroom observations and anecdotal records. For more information about other assessments, refer to the *Assessment Handbook*.

On the following pages you will find passages that may be used for either fluency or running record tests. Both a Teacher Copy and a Student Copy have been provided.

Student Name _____ **Date** _____

Retelling of the Deer and the Hunter
Aesop's Fable

One day, a deer went for a drink at a clear pond. He bent down to take a drink,	19
and he saw himself in the water. He noticed his large horns. He said, "Oh, what	35
great horns I have. They make me look like a king! Yet, look at my legs. They are	53
so thin. What a shame to waste this beautiful crown on a creature with such weak	69
legs."	70
Just then a hunter came close to the pond. He shot an arrow at the deer. The	87
arrow flew by the deer's head, barely missing him. At once, the deer darted away.	102
His light legs made him fast. He dashed into a nearby forest. The deer was not	118
watching where he was going. He was keeping an eye on the hunter. The deer was	134
almost out of sight. Then the deer's horns got tangled in some low branches. The	149
hunter was getting closer. Now the deer's grand horns put him in danger.	162
The deer was stuck in the trees. He started shaking his head, hoping that he	177
could free himself. The hunter was heading straight toward the deer. The deer was	191
frightened.	192
"What a pity!" cried the deer. "What we dislike about ourselves is often what is	207
most useful to us."	211

Fluency Test

[ ] – [ ] = [ ] (wcpm)

Running Record

Oral Reading Accuracy:

$$\frac{[\quad] - [\quad]}{[\quad]} \times 100 = [\quad] \%$$

Reading Rate:

$$\frac{[\quad]}{[\quad]} \times 60 = [\quad] \text{ (wpm)}$$

Retelling of the Deer and the Hunter
Aesop's Fable

One day, a deer went for a drink at a clear pond. He bent down to take a drink, and he saw himself in the water. He noticed his large horns. He said, "Oh, what great horns I have. They make me look like a king! Yet, look at my legs. They are so thin. What a shame to waste this beautiful crown on a creature with such weak legs."

Just then a hunter came close to the pond. He shot an arrow at the deer. The arrow flew by the deer's head, barely missing him. At once, the deer darted away. His light legs made him fast. He dashed into a nearby forest. The deer was not watching where he was going. He was keeping an eye on the hunter. The deer was almost out of sight. Then the deer's horns got tangled in some low branches. The hunter was getting closer. Now the deer's grand horns put him in danger.

The deer was stuck in the trees. He started shaking his head, hoping that he could free himself. The hunter was heading straight toward the deer. The deer was frightened.

"What a pity!" cried the deer. "What we dislike about ourselves is often what is most useful to us."

Student Name _____ **Date** _____

Running Water

We are lucky to have running water in our homes. The early settlers of the	15
United States were not so lucky. Their houses did not have running water. People	29
carried all their drinking water from wells or springs. Carrying water was not	42
work for the weak! A gallon of water weighs eight pounds. In larger settlements,	56
merchants hauled wooden barrels filled with water on wagons and sold it.	68
As more people moved into towns, finding clean water became difficult. Dirty	80
dish and bath water were poured outside. Soon, the ground water became unsafe	93
to drink. In the late 1600s, many public drinking wells were dug. People knew the	108
water from these wells was safe to drink. For a cost, someone would bring safe	123
drinking water to your home.	128
In the 1700s, a new kind of water system was introduced in New York City.	143
Wood logs were carved out in the middle to form wooden pipes. Water from ponds	158
traveled through the logs into the city.	165
By the middle of the 1800s, iron pipes were used. These pipes allowed water	179
to travel great distances. Some of the water traveled forty miles. At first, only a	194
few houses had water taps or sinks. But it did not take long for most people to have	212
indoor water pipes. Running water is a wonderful luxury.	221

Fluency Test

$\boxed{}$ – $\boxed{}$ = $\boxed{}$ (wcpm)

Running Record

Oral Reading Accuracy: Reading Rate:

$\dfrac{\boxed{} - \boxed{}}{\boxed{}}$ × 100 = $\boxed{}$ % $\dfrac{\boxed{}}{\boxed{}}$ × 60 = $\boxed{}$ (wpm)

Running Water

We are lucky to have running water in our homes. The early settlers of the United States were not so lucky. Their houses did not have running water. People carried all their drinking water from wells or springs. Carrying water was not work for the weak! A gallon of water weighs eight pounds. In larger settlements, merchants hauled wooden barrels filled with water on wagons and sold it.

As more people moved into towns, finding clean water became difficult. Dirty dish and bath water were poured outside. Soon, the ground water became unsafe to drink. In the late 1600s, many public drinking wells were dug. People knew the water from these wells was safe to drink. For a cost, someone would bring safe drinking water to your home.

In the 1700s, a new kind of water system was introduced in New York City. Wood logs were carved out in the middle to form wooden pipes. Water from ponds traveled through the logs into the city.

By the middle of the 1800s, iron pipes were used. These pipes allowed water to travel great distances. Some of the water traveled forty miles. At first, only a few houses had water taps or sinks. But it did not take long for most people to have indoor water pipes. Running water is a wonderful luxury.

Student Name _____ **Date** _____

Naming the Foal

Heather tiptoed into the barn to look at the new foal. Heather's favorite horse,	14
Ruby, had just given birth. The sweet smell of hay and horses always reminded her	29
of summer. Heather spent most of her summer days riding horses. In the afternoons,	43
she would help her father clean the stalls. She always had juicy apples to pass out	59
to the horses as treats. But welcoming new foals into the world was Heather's	73
favorite job.	75
Heather's father had spent all night with Ruby, and he was inside now, resting.	89
He had woken Heather up bright and early to tell her about the foal.	103
"Rise and shine!" he said. "I want you to go quietly into the barn. Ruby's baby	119
is here. She will need a name, but you have to see how beautiful she is before you	137
name her."	139
"A girl?" Heather asked. "I only have boys' names—but I'm sure a name will	154
come to me once I see her."	161
When Heather looked into Ruby's stall, she saw the baby horse. The foal	174
could barely stand on her wobbly legs. She was a beauty. Her coat was midnight	189
black, and she had a white mark on her forehead. Her long eyelashes covered her	204
dark eyes. Heather looked deep into her eyes and said, "*Estrella*. It means 'star'	218
in Spanish—to match the diamond on your crown." The foal nodded her head in	233
approval.	234

Fluency Test

[   ] – [   ] = [   ] (wcpm)

Running Record

Oral Reading Accuracy:

$$\frac{[\quad] - [\quad]}{[\quad]} \times 100 = [\quad] \%$$

Reading Rate:

$$\frac{[\quad]}{[\quad]} \times 60 = [\quad] \text{ (wpm)}$$

Naming the Foal

Heather tiptoed into the barn to look at the new foal. Heather's favorite horse, Ruby, had just given birth. The sweet smell of hay and horses always reminded her of summer. Heather spent most of her summer days riding horses. In the afternoons, she would help her father clean the stalls. She always had juicy apples to pass out to the horses as treats. But welcoming new foals into the world was Heather's favorite job.

Heather's father had spent all night with Ruby, and he was inside now, resting. He had woken Heather up bright and early to tell her about the foal.

"Rise and shine!" he said. "I want you to go quietly into the barn. Ruby's baby is here. She will need a name, but you have to see how beautiful she is before you name her."

"A girl?" Heather asked. "I only have boys' names—but I'm sure a name will come to me once I see her."

When Heather looked into Ruby's stall, she saw the baby horse. The foal could barely stand on her wobbly legs. She was a beauty. Her coat was midnight black, and she had a white mark on her forehead. Her long eyelashes covered her dark eyes. Heather looked deep into her eyes and said, "*Estrella*. It means 'star' in Spanish—to match the diamond on your crown." The foal nodded her head in approval.

Student Name _____ **Date** _____

From First Lady to Snack Cakes

One of the most-admired First Ladies in the United States is Dolley Madison.	13
She was born in 1768 in North Carolina. Her parents were Quakers, and she grew	28
up with firm rules. At age 22, she married a lawyer, but sadly, he died from yellow	45
fever a few years later.	50
Then Dolley met James Madison. Soon they were married, and Mrs. Madison	62
decided to give up her Quaker way of life. She started wearing fancy dresses and	77
became a great hostess. James Madison became Secretary of State under Thomas	89
Jefferson. When Jefferson's wife passed away, Dolley became the White House	100
hostess. She had a gift of being gracious.	108
Madison became the fourth President of the United States, and Dolley became	120
the ideal First Lady. She had weekly parties and loved to serve ice cream! She	135
was the first to decorate the White House. When the British took over Washington,	149
D.C., during the war of 1812, she saved a lot of furniture and a painting of George	166
Washington. She also saved important historical papers.	173
Dolley's style and charm made her admired. She had an image as a wonderful	187
hostess, and her name meant good food and great parties. Several companies	199
through the years have used her name to sell their products. There are Dolly	213
Madison snack cakes. At one time there was even Dolly Madison Ice Cream. With	227
such delicious treats still around, it will be hard to forget Dolley Madison.	240

Fluency Test

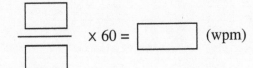

☐ – ☐ = ☐ (wcpm)

Running Record

Oral Reading Accuracy:

☐ – ☐
———— × 100 = ☐ %
☐

Reading Rate:

☐
—— × 60 = ☐ (wpm)
☐

From First Lady to Snack Cakes

One of the most-admired First Ladies in the United States is Dolley Madison. She was born in 1768 in North Carolina. Her parents were Quakers, and she grew up with firm rules. At age 22, she married a lawyer, but sadly, he died from yellow fever a few years later.

Then Dolley met James Madison. Soon they were married, and Mrs. Madison decided to give up her Quaker way of life. She started wearing fancy dresses and became a great hostess. James Madison became Secretary of State under Thomas Jefferson. When Jefferson's wife passed away, Dolley became the White House hostess. She had a gift of being gracious.

Madison became the fourth President of the United States, and Dolley became the ideal First Lady. She had weekly parties and loved to serve ice cream! She was the first to decorate the White House. When the British took over Washington, D.C., during the war of 1812, she saved a lot of furniture and a painting of George Washington. She also saved important historical papers.

Dolley's style and charm made her admired. She had an image as a wonderful hostess, and her name meant good food and great parties. Several companies through the years have used her name to sell their products. There are Dolly Madison snack cakes. At one time there was even Dolly Madison Ice Cream. With such delicious treats still around, it will be hard to forget Dolley Madison.

Student Name _____ Date _____

A Farewell Gift

"I wish I were going with you!" cried Alice.	9
Her best friend looked at her and waved good-bye. "Take care of Boots for me!"	24
Mary answered.	26
Alice held the small cat close to her chest, as she did not want Boots to chase	43
after Mary. A city cat would be unlikely to survive the covered-wagon trip out west,	58
so Boots had a new owner. Alice couldn't believe she would never see Mary again,	73
but Mary had promised she would write often.	81
Mary settled into the back of the covered wagon, thinking about the pioneers	94
who had already traveled west to settle in California. Wagons could break down,	107
and there would be snowstorms and electrical storms. She had read stories about	120
how dangerous it was crossing the Mississippi River and the Rocky Mountains. She	133
wondered if they would encounter any Indians. Then Mary thought about leaving	145
Alice and Boots behind, and a tear ran from her eye.	156
"I have something from Alice," her mother said. "She wanted me to give it to	171
you after we left."	175
Mary carefully opened a small package and found an odd-looking stuffed toy	187
inside. It looked as though Alice had cut up several of her stuffed animals and	202
reassembled parts of them to make a replica of Boots. It looked just like him, with	218
four black paws and a red ribbon around its neck! Mary hugged the animal and felt	234
content. Now both Alice and Boots could comfort her on her journey. Mary opened	248
her journal and began writing Alice a letter.	256

Fluency Test

$\boxed{}$ – $\boxed{}$ = $\boxed{}$ (wcpm)

Running Record

Oral Reading Accuracy: Reading Rate:

$$\frac{\boxed{} - \boxed{}}{\boxed{}} \times 100 = \boxed{} \%$$ $$\frac{\boxed{}}{\boxed{}} \times 60 = \boxed{} \text{ (wpm)}$$

A Farewell Gift

"I wish I were going with you!" cried Alice.

Her best friend looked at her and waved good-bye. "Take care of Boots for me!" Mary answered.

Alice held the small cat close to her chest, as she did not want Boots to chase after Mary. A city cat would be unlikely to survive the covered-wagon trip out west, so Boots had a new owner. Alice couldn't believe she would never see Mary again, but Mary had promised she would write often.

Mary settled into the back of the covered wagon, thinking about the pioneers who had already traveled west to settle in California. Wagons could break down, and there would be snowstorms and electrical storms. She had read stories about how dangerous it was crossing the Mississippi River and the Rocky Mountains. She wondered if they would encounter any Indians. Then Mary thought about leaving Alice and Boots behind, and a tear ran from her eye.

"I have something from Alice," her mother said. "She wanted me to give it to you after we left."

Mary carefully opened a small package and found an odd-looking stuffed toy inside. It looked as though Alice had cut up several of her stuffed animals and reassembled parts of them to make a replica of Boots. It looked just like him, with four black paws and a red ribbon around its neck! Mary hugged the animal and felt content. Now both Alice and Boots could comfort her on her journey. Mary opened her journal and began writing Alice a letter.

Student Name _____ **Date** _____

Ride in Space

She was strapped into the space shuttle *Challenger*, excited about lift-off.	11
Within seconds, Sally Ride would be the first American woman in space.	23
Sally Ride was born in California. Her first dream was to become a great tennis	38
player. She practiced hard, but she knew that tennis would not be her career. Sally	53
decided to go to college and study science, her second love.	64
When Sally finished school, she saw an ad in the newspaper. NASA was	77
looking for astronauts. This sounded interesting to her, so she applied for the job.	91
Thousands of people were also interested in the job. Only thirty-five people were	104
chosen and five of those were women. Sally Ride was one of them.	117
First, Sally needed training to become an astronaut. She learned about gravity	129
and being weightless. She practiced jumping with a parachute and surviving in the	142
water. She also learned about the space shuttle.	150
The day finally arrived. On June 18, 1983, Sally Ride boarded *Challenger,*	162
ready for her first mission. Once in space, she did experiments. She worked the	176
spacecraft's robotic arm. She used hand controls to work the arm.	187
Sally was in space six days. She slept while floating! The body has no weight	202
in space, so it floats. Space food is bland, but she brought some peanut butter and	218
bread. A year later, Sally took another ride in *Challenger.*	228
Today, Dr. Sally Ride teaches. She also writes children's books. *To Space and*	241
Back is her book about her experience. Dr. Ride still helps with the space program	256
and encourages young students to get interested in science.	265

Fluency Test

[ ] – [ ] = [ ] (wcpm)

Running Record

Oral Reading Accuracy: Reading Rate:

$$\frac{[\quad] - [\quad]}{[\quad]} \times 100 = [\quad] \%$$

$$\frac{[\quad]}{[\quad]} \times 60 = [\quad] \text{ (wpm)}$$

Ride in Space

She was strapped into the space shuttle *Challenger*, excited about lift-off. Within seconds, Sally Ride would be the first American woman in space.

Sally Ride was born in California. Her first dream was to become a great tennis player. She practiced hard, but she knew that tennis would not be her career. Sally decided to go to college and study science, her second love.

When Sally finished school, she saw an ad in the newspaper. NASA was looking for astronauts. This sounded interesting to her, so she applied for the job. Thousands of people were also interested in the job. Only thirty-five people were chosen and five of those were women. Sally Ride was one of them.

First, Sally needed training to become an astronaut. She learned about gravity and being weightless. She practiced jumping with a parachute and surviving in the water. She also learned about the space shuttle.

The day finally arrived. On June 18, 1983, Sally Ride boarded *Challenger*, ready for her first mission. Once in space, she did experiments. She worked the spacecraft's robotic arm. She used hand controls to work the arm.

Sally was in space six days. She slept while floating! The body has no weight in space, so it floats. Space food is bland, but she brought some peanut butter and bread. A year later, Sally took another ride in *Challenger*.

Today, Dr. Sally Ride teaches. She also writes children's books. *To Space and Back* is her book about her experience. Dr. Ride still helps with the space program and encourages young students to get interested in science.

NAME _____ **DATE** _____

Scott Foresman
Benchmark Test
Unit 1
Turning Points

PEARSON

Glenview, Illinois
Boston, Massachusetts
Chandler, Arizona
Upper Saddle River, New Jersey

ISBN-13: 978-0-328-53744-0
ISBN-10:   0-328-53744-6

1 2 3 4 5 6 7 8 9 10 V011 19 18 17 16 15 14 13 12 11 10
CC1

Directions

What do you do when you live in California and there is no snow in December? Read about how one family solved the problem. Then do Numbers 1 through 11.

Let It Snow

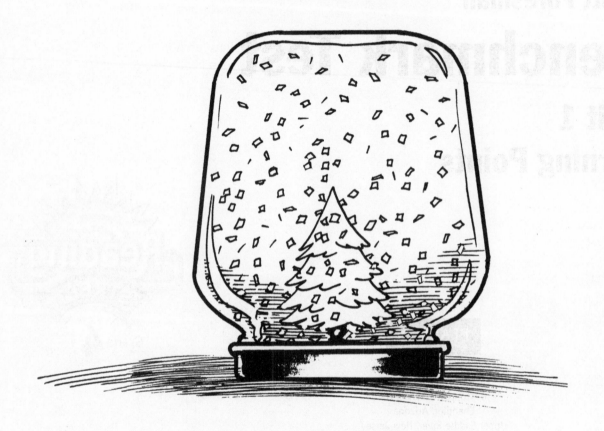

Late last summer, the Young family moved. They left their small town in Maine and went to San Diego, California. San Diego was warm and sunny. There were wonderful beaches and parks. The three children liked their new school. The parents had great new jobs. Everybody seemed happy.

Sometime in December, ten-year-old Emily saw that her mother seemed a little sad. "All this sunshine is getting me down," her mother said. "I know San Diego has 360 days a year of good weather. That's too many for me. I miss stormy days and skies. How can it be December without any snow? I really miss the snow."

Emily wanted to cheer up her mother. She talked it over with her older brother, Jacob, and her younger sister, Morgan. They knew that they could not take their mother to the snow. It was too far away. But maybe they could bring the snow to her.

Emily had the idea of making a snow globe. A snow globe is a glass container with a winter scene inside it. When you shake the globe, it looks like snow is falling. Their father helped them find what they needed: glitter, glue, baby oil, and an empty baby food jar. Jacob offered a tiny pine tree from his train set.

They glued the tree to the inside of the baby food jar's cap. To help it stick better, Jacob first sanded a spot in the center of the cap. Next, Emily filled the jar with baby oil. Morgan added a bit of glitter. Dad spread some glue along the rim of the cap. Then he carefully screwed the cap on the jar.

Morgan giggled at the sight of the tree hanging upside-down in the jar. "Let's give it to Mom right away," she begged. Everyone agreed. They turned the globe right side up. Then they wrapped it in bright paper.

Singing "Let It Snow," the three children walked out to their mother, who was working in the garden. They shouted "Surprise!" as Morgan handed her the package.

1   **The author wrote this selection to**

A   persuade the reader to make a snow globe.

B   express feelings about snow.

C   entertain the reader with a story about a family.

D   explain how snow falls in a snow storm.

2   **What was the biggest difference between the Youngs' old home and their new one?**

F   The schools were better near their new home.

G   The parents preferred their new jobs to their old ones.

H   Their new house was bigger than their old house.

J   The weather was sunnier at their new home.

3   **Instead of placing a tiny pine tree inside the snow globe, the children could have used**

A   a sailboat.

B   a palm tree.

C   a pair of skis.

D   a surfboard.

GO ON

4   **What was the first step in making the snow globe?**

    F   sanding the lid

    G   adding the glitter

    H   washing out the jar

    J   finding the materials

5   **When the children shouted "Surprise!" their mother most likely**

    A   shouted in anger.

    B   looked up happily.

    C   started to cry.

    D   waved them away.

6   **Why did the children make the snow globe?**

    F   to cheer up their mother

    G   to have fun making something

    H   to complete a school assignment

    J   to spend some time with their father

7   **From her actions in the story, you can tell that Emily**

    A   does very well in school.

    B   has a lot of friends.

    C   is good at sports.

    D   has a kind heart.

8   **Which of these events happened third in the selection?**

    F   Emily had an idea.

    G   The children's father found supplies.

    H   The children gave their mother the snow globe.

    J   The family moved from Maine to San Diego.

9   **The children probably chose to sing "Let It Snow" because this song**

    A   gave a hint about the gift.

    B   was their favorite song.

    C   was playing on the radio at the time.

    D   had been taught for the school concert.

10 **What is another good title for this story?**

    F "A Stormy Day"

    G "A Gift for Mom"

    H "All About Snow Globes"

    J "Sun in December"

11 **Based on the selection, which of these did the Young children most likely experience first?**

    A They went to California beaches and made sand castles.

    B They packed their things and moved to San Diego.

    C They made a snowman in their backyard.

    D They received thanks from their mother for the snow globe.

GO ON

Directions

Write your answer to Question A on the lines below. Base your answer on "Let It Snow."

A Emily's mother really missed the snow when she moved to San Diego. What do you like best about snow? If you live in a place where it doesn't snow, tell what you think you would like, based on what you've learned about snow. Give details to support your answer.

_____

_____

_____

_____

_____

_____

_____

_____

_____

Directions

Read about how each state's license plate tells a little about that state. Then do Numbers 12 through 22.

State License Plates

FLORIDA
123 456
SUNSHINE STATE

Each state in our country is special. A state's license plates are one way for a state to show how it is special.

Some states have simple plates. California's plate has the state name written in what looks like bold handwriting. Connecticut's plate has a state outline and says "Constitution State." Similarly, Delaware's plate says "The First State."

Some states' plates show goods that come from those states. Georgia shows a peach. Florida shows a flowering orange tree branch. Idaho's plate says "Famous Potatoes." Wisconsin calls itself "America's Dairyland."

GO ON

Some states feature state birds or flowers on their plates. Others show special places in the state. New Hampshire's plate shows the Old Man of the Mountain. South Dakota's plate shows Mount Rushmore. Utah's plate shows the Centennial Arch. Vermont, Colorado, and Oregon have mountain peaks on their plates. Rhode Island, the Ocean State, has a large wave.

Some states teach history lessons. Virginia's plate celebrates the settlement of Jamestown 400 years ago. Illinois's plate says "Land of Lincoln," with President Lincoln's picture. Texas's plate celebrates its past and present. Its plate shows a cowboy, oil wells, and the space shuttle. Some states even disagree a little over history. The Wright brothers were born in Ohio. Ohio's plate says "Birthplace of Aviation." However, the brothers first flew in North Carolina. Those plates say "First in Flight."

Alabama is the only state to use a song on its license plate. The song is "Stars Fell on Alabama." The title is shown with stars and musical notes.

Some plates promote their states. Maine's plate says "Vacationland." Kentucky's says "Unbridled Spirit."

It is possible to print attractive pictures on license plates. New Mexico's plate shows a balloon rising over the desert. Nebraska's plate shows birds flying above the plains.

In 2000, Pennsylvania became the first state to put its Web site on its license plate. West Virginia, Florida, and Georgia followed Pennsylvania's lead. The trend is likely to continue.

Why all the variety around the country? It's because people are generally proud of their state and want to draw attention to it. These days a license plate does more than just identify a car.

12   **What is the main idea of the selection?**

   F   Every state requires cars to have a license plate.

   G   Many states have added Web sites to their plates.

   H   State license plates are as varied as the states themselves.

   J   Some state license plates are better looking than others.

13   **Which was the first state to take advantage of the popularity of computers?**

   A   West Virginia

   B   Florida

   C   California

   D   Pennsylvania

14   **Which of these is a statement of opinion?**

F   Each state in our country is special.

G   Some states' plates show goods that come from those states.

H   Idaho's plate says "Famous Potatoes."

J   Alabama is the only state to use a song on its license plate.

15   **The author wrote this selection to**

A   entertain the reader with funny stories about license plates.

B   persuade the reader that each state is interesting.

C   provide information about states and their license plates.

D   express feelings about state sayings.

16   **How does the author organize his examples?**

F   by listing states in alphabetical order

G   by grouping together all the states in a given region

H   by giving the oldest plates first and then moving to newer ones

J   by grouping states that design their plates in similar ways

17   **The author did not include every state. The most likely reason is that**

A   some states do not have license plates.

B   the states' plates not included are similar to those that are included.

C   there was no information available about some states' plates.

D   he did not like the license plates of some states.

18   **Which state's plate has a picture of a famous person?**

F   Maine

G   Illinois

H   Kentucky

J   North Carolina

GO ON

19 Based on the selection, which two states claim the same historical event?

A   Ohio and North Carolina

B   Connecticut and Delaware

C   Virginia and Illinois

D   Maine and Kentucky

20 How are the plates of Nebraska and New Mexico alike?

F   They have scenic pictures.

G   They show famous parks.

H   They are very simple.

J   They are the same color.

21 The author's purpose is achieved mainly by

A   quoting several experts.

B   including opinions of ordinary people.

C   building suspense.

D   providing many examples.

22 You would most likely see a selection like this in

F   an encyclopedia.

G   a magazine.

H   a private journal.

J   a local newspaper.

Directions

Write your answer to Question B on the lines below. Base your answer on the two selections you have read.

B   Compare the author's purpose for writing each selection. Provide support from each reading selection for your answer.

_____

_____

_____

_____

_____

_____

_____

_____

_____

_____

PART 2: VOCABULARY

Directions

Mark your answer choice for Numbers 23 through 32.

23 Which word has a suffix?

A   along

B   away

C   Emily

D   friendly

24 Some states' plates show *goods* that come from that state. What is a synonym for *goods* in this sentence?

F   machines

G   citizens

H   products

J   fruit

25 Which word has a suffix like that in *pitiful?*

A   fuller

B   fullback

C   fulfilled

D   cheerful

26 Connecticut's license plate has a state *outline* and says "Constitution State." The *outline* shows

F   the most important facts about the state.

G   the location of the state.

H   the earliest history of the state.

J   the shape of the state.

27 Which word or words could best replace *generally* in the following sentence?

It's because people are generally proud of their state.

A   not generatly

B   generateful

C   in general

D   un general

28 On Alabama's license plate, a song title is shown with stars and *musical* notes. Which word has a suffix like that in *musical?*

   F   almost

   G   musician

   H   comical

   J   animal

29 Which of the following is the meaning of the word *stick* as used in this sentence?

   To help it stick better, Jacob first sanded a spot in the center of the cap.

   A   to attach to something

   B   to be noticed somewhere

   C   to keep doing something

   D   to push into something

30 Which word could best replace *attractive* in the following sentence?

   It is possible to print attractive pictures on license plates.

   F   colorful

   G   lasting

   H   tiny

   J   lovely

31 Which meaning of the word *miss* is used in the following sentence?

   I miss stormy days and skies.

   A   to fail to hit

   B   to remember with sadness

   C   to fail to see or notice

   D   to leave out

32 Which word has a suffix like that in *inventive?*

   F   creative

   G   lively

   H   forgive

   J   drive

PART 3: WRITING CONVENTIONS

Directions

Mark your answer choice for Numbers 33 through 40.

In Numbers 33 through 36, read each sentence. Mark the answer that best describes the sentence.

33 I really miss the snow!

    A declarative sentence

    B interrogative sentence

    C exclamatory sentence

    D imperative sentence

34 Some license plates teach history lessons.

    F declarative sentence

    G interrogative sentence

    H exclamatory sentence

    J imperative sentence

35 They all shouted as Morgan handed her the package.

    A simple sentence

    B complex sentence

    C compound sentence

    D compound-complex sentence

36 Some states' license plates feature state birds or flowers.

    F simple sentence

    G complex sentence

    H compound sentence

    J compound-complex sentence

37 Which of the following sentences is a compound sentence?

 A Emily filled the jar with baby oil, and Morgan added a bit of glitter.

 B Mrs. Young was sad because she missed the snow.

 C The Young family left Maine and moved to San Diego, California.

 D A snow globe is a glass container with a winter scene inside it.

38 Which of the following sentences is a complex sentence?

 F Maine's plates show a chickadee, and Mississippi's plates show a magnolia.

 G Both New Hampshire and South Dakota have special places on their plates.

 H States can now print pictures on their license plates.

 J After Pennsylvania put its Web site on its plate, other states did too.

39 What is the simple subject of this sentence?

 Rhode Island, the Ocean State, has a large wave.

 A Rhode Island

 B Island

 C Rhode Island, the Ocean State

 D has

40 What is the complete predicate of this sentence?

 The title is shown with stars and musical notes.

 F The title

 G is

 H is shown

 J is shown with stars and musical notes

PART 4: WRITING

PROMPT

In "Let It Snow," the family prepares a surprise for Mrs. Young. Think about a time you prepared a surprise for somebody or somebody prepared a surprise for you. Tell the story of what happened. Be sure to include how you felt about what happened.

CHECKLIST FOR WRITERS

_____ Did I think about a time when I surprised someone or someone surprised me?

_____ Did I take notes about the surprise and how it made me feel?

_____ Did I organize my writing in a logical way?

_____ Did I tell my feelings about what happened?

_____ Did I use words and details that clearly express my ideas?

_____ Do my sentences make sense?

_____ Did I check my sentences for proper grammar and punctuation?

_____ Did I check my spelling?

_____ Did I make sure my paper is the way I want readers to read it?

NAME _____   DATE _____

Scott Foresman

Benchmark Test

Unit 2
Teamwork

PEARSON

Glenview, Illinois
Boston, Massachusetts
Chandler, Arizona
Upper Saddle River, New Jersey

ISBN-13: 978-0-328-53745-7
ISBN-10:   0-328-53745-4

1 2 3 4 5 6 7 8 9 10 V011 19 18 17 16 15 14 13 12 11 10
CC1

ISBN-13: 978-0-328-53745-7
ISBN-10:   0-328-53745-4

EAN

9 780328 537457

90000>

*D*irections
Read this selection about blueberries. Then do Numbers 1 through 11.

The All-American Berry

The blueberry deserves the title of all-American berry. The blueberry has been growing in North America for thousands of years. It is a native plant and now grows in thirty-five different states in the United States. Almost all the blueberries grown in the world are grown here in the United States. Americans grow about 300 million pounds of blueberries every year. Blueberry pancakes, blueberry muffins, and blueberry pies are all favorites.

National Blueberry Month is celebrated in July. That is when there are plenty of fresh, ripe berries. Most blueberries are picked then, but you can find them at the market all year long. There are canned blueberries on the shelf. There are frozen berries in the freezer case. There are even dried blueberries to eat as a snack.

Native Americans picked blueberries. They ate them in the summer, and they made tea from the leaves. They drank blueberry juice to cure coughs. They also dried berries for winter consumption. Some dried berries were pounded to a powder; then the blueberry powder was mixed with cornmeal and water to make a blueberry mush. The berries were also added to dried meat. Blueberries helped to ensure good health through the long, tough winters.

When settlers from Europe arrived in North America, they learned about blueberries from the Native Americans. The settlers liked the taste of the sweet berries. It is very possible that blueberry mush was on the first Thanksgiving menu. In later years, the settlers added milk, butter, and sugar to the mush.

You can make blueberry mush yourself. Here is the recipe. Be careful, and have an adult help you.

1. Combine 2 cups of water and 2 cups of milk in a pan. Heat until little bubbles form on the edge of the pan.
2. Add 1 cup of cornmeal slowly and keep stirring. Add a little salt.
3. Cover the pan. Turn the heat to low. Cook the mush until it gets thick. Stir it from time to time.
4. Take the pan off the stove. Add about 1/4 cup of honey or maple syrup. Stir it in well.
5. Add a pint of washed fresh blueberries.

Note: You can use 2 cups of frozen or canned berries instead of fresh ones. Defrost frozen berries between two layers of paper towel. Drain canned blueberries. Undrained blueberries would turn the mush blue.

1 **What is the topic of this selection?**
  A cornmeal mush
  B Native Americans' foods
  C European settlers' foods
  D blueberries

2 **The main idea of the third paragraph is that Native Americans**
  F dried blueberries and made blueberry powder.
  G made and ate blueberry mush.
  H taught settlers about blueberries.
  J used blueberries in many ways.

3 **Compared to the first blueberry mush they ate, the mush made by the settlers later on was probably**
  A thicker.
  B healthier.
  C sweeter.
  D saltier.

GO ON

4 Which sentence in the first paragraph is a statement of opinion?

F The blueberry deserves the title of all-American berry.

G The blueberry has been growing in North America for thousands of years.

H Almost all the blueberries grown in the world are grown here in the United States.

J Americans grow about 300 million pounds of blueberries every year.

5 What is the last step in making blueberry mush?

A mixing the milk and water

B adding the blueberries

C adding the maple syrup or honey

D slowly stirring in the cornmeal

6 In making blueberry mush, when do you cover the pan?

F as soon as you turn on the heat

G just before you add the cornmeal

H just after you add the cornmeal

J when you take the pot off the stove

7 Why did the author include the recipe for blueberry mush?

A It is a very popular dessert for people to eat.

B It lets the reader share the settlers' experience.

C It is the best way to celebrate National Blueberry Month.

D It is a simple way to store blueberries for later use.

8 Which statement is supported by information from the selection?

F North America produces most of the world's blueberries.

G Blueberries will grow only in North America.

H Americans eat more blueberries than any other fruit.

J The most popular way to eat blueberries is in pancakes.

9 Why should you have an adult help you with the recipe?

A because you need two people to stir the pot

B so you can eat while the adult cooks

C so you do not burn yourself

D because an adult has made the mush before

10   The author wrote this selection to

    F   express feelings about blueberries.

    G   present information about blueberries.

    H   entertain readers with a funny story about blueberries.

    J   persuade readers that blueberries are healthful.

11   You can tell from the selection that blueberries grow

    A   best in the forest.

    B   ripe in autumn.

    C   only in the South.

    D   in many states.

Write your answer to Question A on the lines below. Base your answer on "The All-American Berry."

> **A**   Think about making blueberry mush. Explain why it would be important to read the entire recipe before you begin.
>
> _____
>
> _____
>
> _____
>
> _____
>
> _____
>
> _____
>
> _____
>
> _____
>
> _____
>
> _____

Directions

Read this selection about planning and building a playground. Then do Numbers 12 through 22.

GRAND OPENING OF TOWN PLAYGROUND

Yesterday afternoon, Pine Lake marked the opening of its new playground. There were balloons, speeches, and a lot of prizes. The people of Pine Lake are proud of their new playground. They are also proud that everybody worked together to build it.

It all started last September in a fourth-grade classroom. The teacher, Miss Green, asked her class to think about Pine Lake. Miss Green wondered how the town could be better. Her students decided that a playground would enhance the town.

Some students drew pictures of a new playground. Others wrote stories about it. Students in other classes got excited about the idea too. They talked to family members about the project. Everyone worked to make the dream come true.

A group of parents met to work on park plans. Mrs. Schein said, "I was sure many people would lend a hand. We sent out a letter asking people to list ways they could help. A lot of people answered the letter. Some said they could build things. Others agreed to pick up supplies. An artist made a poster. Neighborhood businesses gave money and goods."

In January, the town had a planning day. The children had many ideas about the playground. They knew what they wanted. Sue Wing, a builder, wrote down the ideas. She spent the next month drawing the design. Wing said, "Designing the playground was the most fun I have had in years. The kids had such good ideas."

GO ON

March was building month. Wood, sand, and other goods were ordered. Helpers picked up the supplies and dropped them off beside the lake. Tom Smith used his bulldozer to level the ground at the site.

Last Saturday, the people of Pine Lake built the playground. The weather was warm and sunny. It was a great day for building. More than two hundred people showed up to help. Some people were unavailable, but everybody who was there went to work. By the end of the day, the job was done. Pine Lake had its new playground.

12 **What is the main idea of this selection?**

F There were balloons, prizes, and speeches at the grand opening.

G Pine Lake needed a new playground for the town.

H Miss Green's class was responsible for the new playground.

J The people of Pine Lake built a new playground together.

13 **You would most likely see writing like this in**

A a local newspaper.

B an encyclopedia.

C an atlas.

D a sports magazine.

14 **What happened in January?**

F The idea of a playground was introduced.

G The playground was built.

H The playground materials were ordered.

J The town planned the playground.

15 **What did Tom Smith do for the playground?**

A He led the parents' group.

B He designed the playground.

C He gave money.

D He leveled the ground.

16 The idea of having a playground came from

    F a group of parents.

    G Miss Green.

    H a group of students.

    J Sue Wing.

17 You can tell from the last paragraph on page 7 that Sue Wing

    A had built a playground in Pine Lake before.

    B used the students' ideas in her design.

    C had a lot of trouble drawing the design.

    D did not like all of the students' ideas.

18 This selection shows how people can gain from

    F playing games.

    G holding a contest.

    H doing research.

    J working together.

19 The last paragraph of the selection is mainly about the

    A grand opening of the playground.

    B design of the playground.

    C actual building of the playground.

    D uses for the playground.

20 Which of the following types of details does the author use to present information?

    F quotes from people involved

    G diagrams of the playground's design

    H lists of the work required

    J facts from national experts

GO ON

21 The parents' group wrote a letter asking for help from

A town officials.

B construction companies.

C Miss Green's class.

D Pine Lake residents and businesses.

22 The effect of the students' pictures and stories was to

F create prizes for the opening day.

G get people excited about the idea.

H raise money for the project.

J inspire Sue Wing's design.

Directions

Write your answer to Question B on the lines below. Base your answer on the two selections you have read.

B Think about the Native Americans in "The All-American Berry" and the people of Pine Lake in "Grand Opening of Town Playground." In what ways were the Native Americans like the people of Pine Lake? Use details and examples from the selections to support your answer.

WRITING ACROSS TEXTS

_____

_____

_____

_____

_____

_____

_____

_____

PART 2: VOCABULARY

Directions

Mark your answer choice for Numbers 23 through 32.

23 The first selection explained that the blueberry is a *native* plant. What does *native* mean?

   A was brought here first by the settlers

   B has always been here

   C is well-liked by the people who live here

   D makes people healthy

24 In the second selection, Miss Green wondered how the town could be better. Her students decided a playground would *enhance* the town. The word *enhance* means

   F destroy.

   G improve.

   H be costly for.

   J shrink.

25 *National* Blueberry Month is celebrated in July. What is the base word of *national?*

   A nation

   B nat

   C tion

   D al

26 Americans grow about 300 million pounds of blueberries *every year*. What single word could replace *every year* in this sentence?

   F yearable

   G yearal

   H yearful

   J yearly

27 Native Americans drank blueberry juice to *cure* coughs. Another word for *cure* is

   A soften.

   B increase.

   C spread.

   D heal.

28 The recipe for blueberry mush says that *undrained* blueberries would turn the mush blue. *Undrained* means

   F   not drained.

   G   drained only once.

   H   drained too much.

   J   badly drained.

29 An *artist* made a poster for the new playground. In which word does *ist* mean the same as it does in *artist*?

   A   list

   B   history

   C   tourist

   D   sister

30 There are *canned* blueberries in grocery stores. *Canned* means

   F   able to.

   G   for sale.

   H   sweet.

   J   put in a can.

31 Native Americans dried berries for winter *consumption*. What does *consumption* mean?

   A   harvesting

   B   using up

   C   purchase

   D   illness

32 Some people were *unavailable* to help build the playground. *Unavailable* means

   F   not happy.

   G   not able to help.

   H   ready to help.

   J   not helpful.

PART 3: WRITING CONVENTIONS

Directions

Mark your answer choice for Numbers 33 through 40.

33 Which word in this sentence is a noun?

They talked to family members about it.

A talked

B to

C members

D about

34 Which noun names something that cannot be seen?

F sand

G playground

H idea

J builder

35 Blueberries can be found on the *shelf* in the store. What is the plural form of *shelf*?

A shelfves

B shelfs

C shelfes

D shelves

36 "The All-American Berry" uses the singular word *blueberry* and its plural form, *blueberries*. Which word forms its plural the same way *blueberry* does?

F key

G sky

H boy

J ray

37 The word *children* is an irregular plural. Which word also has an irregular plural?

   A mouse

   B horse

   C fox

   D giraffe

38 Which word or words from "Grand Opening of Town Playground" is a common noun?

   F Pine Lake

   G Miss Green

   H businesses

   J Saturday

39 Sue Wing drew the design for the playground. What is the correct way to refer to her design?

   A Sue Wings design

   B Sue Wing's design

   C Sue Wings' design

   D Sue's Wing design

40 Which sentence is written correctly?

   F The playground design used the childrens ideas.

   G The playground design used the children's ideas.

   H The playground design used the childrens ideas.'

   J The playground design used the childrens' ideas.

PART 4: WRITING

PROMPT

Both "The All-American Berry" and "Grand Opening of Town Playground" tell about things people know how to make or do. Think of something you know how to do. It could be cooking a meal, throwing a football, building a birdhouse, playing a game, or something else. Write to explain how to do this activity.

CHECKLIST FOR WRITERS

_____ Did I think about something that I know how to do?

_____ Did I take notes about the activity before I started writing?

_____ Did I write my explanation in the correct order?

_____ Did I use words and details that clearly express my ideas?

_____ Do my sentences make sense?

_____ Did I check my sentences for proper grammar and punctuation?

_____ Did I check my spelling?

_____ Did I make sure my paper is the way I want readers to read it?

NAME _____   DATE _____

Scott Foresman
Benchmark Test
Unit 3
Patterns in Nature

PEARSON

Glenview, Illinois
Boston, Massachusetts
Chandler, Arizona
Upper Saddle River, New Jersey

ISBN-13: 978-0-328-53746-4
ISBN-10:   0-328-53746-2

1 2 3 4 5 6 7 8 9 10 V011 19 18 17 16 15 14 13 12 11 10
CC1

ISBN-13: 978-0-328-53746-4
ISBN-10:   0-328-53746-2

EAN

9 780328 537464

90000>

PART 1: COMPREHENSION

Directions

Think about the beauty of individual snowflakes and read this selection about them. Then do Numbers 1 through 11.

Snowflakes

It's been said that no two snowflakes are alike. But how could anyone know? Who could count all the snowflakes that fall each winter in Alaska? If you haven't seen them all, how would you know that no two snowflakes were the same?

Kenneth Libbrecht, who has spent years studying snowflakes, has been asked this question. Based on his years as a scientist, he thinks no two snowflakes are exactly alike but realizes that telling them apart is difficult.

That does not mean that snowflakes don't look the same to the human eye. They often do. Even someone looking at a snowflake through a normal microscope won't notice differences between snowflakes. It takes a very powerful microscope to show those differences.

One thing is certain: all snowflakes are beautiful. They come in dozens of shapes and types. Think of them as frozen pieces of art that are very small. Their many shapes, seen in photographs made through a microscope, are truly fascinating and lovely.

The closer you look at any pair of snowflakes, the more you see they are not the same. It's the same as when you look at other things that are supposed to look alike. For example, think about identical twins. If you look at the faces of twins from thirty feet away, you can't see any difference. Look closely enough, and you are sure to discover that they are not exactly the same.

What's really interesting about snowflakes is that you could be part of one. Water evaporates from your skin and is also carried in the air you breathe out. The water that leaves your body and goes into the air could someday come back to Earth as rain or snow. That tiny snowflake that falls on your nose could have started out right there.

Who cares if no two snowflakes are exactly the same? Isn't their beauty more interesting? Think of them as amazing, tiny pieces of art that happen to be ice. Think of how they have been loved by poets and scientists and children playing in the snow for hundreds of years.

1 **Why did the author write "Snowflakes"?**

A to show how most snowflakes are created

B to explain what snowflakes look like

C to share feelings and facts about snowflakes

D to describe how snowflakes are like art

2 **Which sentence from the selection is a statement of opinion?**

F Kenneth Libbrecht, who has spent years studying snowflakes, has been asked this question.

G The water that leaves your body and goes into the air could someday come back to Earth as rain or snow.

H Water evaporates from your skin and is also carried in the air you breathe out.

J One thing is certain: all snowflakes are beautiful.

3 **What is the purpose of the first paragraph?**

A to make readers start thinking about snowflakes

B to answer questions that most readers have

C to make readers imagine winter in Alaska

D to prove that the author knows about snowflakes

GO ON

4 What is the sixth paragraph mostly about?

F why its snows instead of rains

G the water that is in snowflakes

H how to catch a snowflake on your nose

J your skin and your breath

5 According to the selection, what do all snowflakes have in common?

A thickness

B beauty

C weight

D shape

6 Which tool would best help you prove the following statement of fact?

No two snowflakes are exactly alike.

F a ruler

G a calculator

H a microscope

J a thermometer

7 What makes Kenneth Libbrecht an expert on snowflakes?

A He has studied snowflakes for a long time.

B He thinks that each snowflake is special.

C He thinks snowflakes are very beautiful.

D He has traveled to Alaska to study snowflakes.

8 What is the main purpose of paragraph five?

F to tell a way that twins are like snowflakes

G to show how twins are really identical

H to prove that we know no two snowflakes are alike

J to give an example of small differences between two things

9 According to the selection, what would make a poet want to write a poem about snowflakes?

A an interest in the weather

B a knowledge of science

C an interest in how they look

D a memory of a childhood event

10 What is the main idea of the last paragraph?

    F   We should enjoy snowflakes for what they are.

    G   We should tell people that snowflakes are art.

    H   Snowflakes have been popular for hundreds of years.

    J   Snowflakes are something that all children like.

11 Who would be most able to show the differences between two snowflakes?

    A   twins

    B   children

    C   a scientist

    D   a poet

Directions

Write your answer to Question A on the lines below. Base your answer on "Snowflakes."

A   What do you think about snowflakes? Do you agree with the author that they are amazing pieces of art? Give details to explain your answer.

_____

_____

_____

_____

_____

_____

_____

_____

_____

Blending In

One of the ways I stay alive is by blending into the woods where I live. Right now it is autumn. I am standing with five other deer from my herd, deep in a wooded area of a state park. I can hear people coming, hiking down a trail. They are very far away right now, but they are getting closer. We are all listening and watching.

These hikers would love to see us, but they probably won't. We blend in with the fallen leaves and fir tree bark and the overall color of our habitat. The other animals around us—rabbits and squirrels, mostly—blend in too. We prefer to live unnoticed, blending in with our surroundings. Being camouflaged makes our lives easier.

The hikers are now about fifty feet away, but they do not notice us. They are busy talking and enjoying themselves while we are completely still. We can see them and hear them and smell them, but they walk by without knowing we are here. Even if they stood and stared in our direction, it might take them a while to make out our shapes. We are completely still.

GO ON

Other animals here in this forest change color depending on the season. There is a rabbit that is grayish-brown in summer, but turns white in winter. Changing color makes it a lot harder for the foxes and owls to see her, just as my fur makes it harder for mountain lions to spot me in the forest.

One of the strangest insects I see in the woods is called the walking stick. I have seen them up close, but only when they move. They look so much like an actual twig on a tree that it's hard to believe they aren't made of wood. You can be one foot away from a walking stick and never even know it's there. The walking stick uses camouflage for the same reason I do: it keeps us alive.

Not all of us can fight our enemies. Often we cannot outrun them either. To keep from becoming food, we use whatever strategies we can to keep ourselves safe. For me and for many other forest animals, camouflage is the answer. It helps us to live longer and happier lives. Nobody wants to be somebody else's dinner.

12 **Who is the narrator of this selection?**

F a hiker

G a park ranger

H a forest animal

J a scientist

13 **Which of these would best help you prove the following statement of fact?**

Other animals in this forest change color depending on the season.

A biography

B encyclopedia

C atlas

D dictionary

14 **What is one reason that the hikers did not see the deer?**

F The hikers were talking to each other.

G The hikers were standing still.

H The hikers were watching where they walked.

J The hikers were looking for different animals.

15 **Based on the selection, you can generalize that**

A all animals use camouflage to hide from their enemies.

B many animals use camouflage to hide from their enemies.

C most animals can outrun their enemies.

D no animals fight their enemies to stay alive.

16 **What makes the walking stick blend in with the woods?**

   F   It never moves.

   G   It is very small.

   H   It looks like a twig.

   J   It is made of wood.

17 **What is the main purpose of the last paragraph?**

   A   to describe the meaning of camouflage

   B   to explain why animals like to stay alive

   C   to give reasons why animals use camouflage

   D   to show that some animals eat other animals

18 **What allows animals to blend in with the forest?**

   F   their senses

   G   their diet

   H   their speed

   J   their colors

19 **What causes the rabbit mentioned in the fourth paragraph to change color?**

   A   fear

   B   foxes

   C   seasons

   D   noise

20 **Using camouflage is best described as**

   F   way to survive.

   G   an escape route.

   H   a feeding pattern.

   J   an insect behavior.

GO ON

21 Camouflage helps an animal
 A stay warm in the winter.
 B blend into its surroundings.
 C run fast and catch its prey.
 D eat well and sleep well.

22 Even with good camouflage, to be hidden a deer must
 F remain very still.
 G walk quickly.
 H learn to fight.
 J stay close to the ground.

Directions

B How can looking closely change the way we see things? Use details and examples from both selections to support your answer.

WRITING ACROSS TEXTS

_____

_____

_____

_____

_____

_____

_____

_____

_____

_____

PART 2: VOCABULARY

Directions
Mark your answer choice for Numbers 23 through 32.

23 Which word fits best in the following sentence?

> The rabbit's _____ is white.

  A fur

  B far

  C for

  D fir

24 Which sentence is written correctly?

  F I am going to right a letter.

  G Sue wears a ring on her write hand.

  H Joe likes to right his papers in ink.

  J All of your answers were right.

25 Snowflakes' many shapes are truly *fascinating* and lovely. What does *fascinating* mean?

  A interesting

  B amusing

  C silent

  D close

26 "Blending In" is about how animals use *camouflage*. An example of *camouflage* is

  F an eagle's wide-spread wings.

  G an owl's sharp eyes.

  H a polar bear's white fur.

  J a squirrel's bushy tail.

27 What is the suffix of the word *beautiful?*

  A beau

  B beauty

  C ul

  D ful

28 Think of snowflakes as *amazing* tiny pieces of art that happen to be ice. What is the meaning of *amazing?*

F small

G thin

H expensive

J wonderful

29 Which meaning of the word *spot* is used in the following sentence?

It makes it a lot harder for the foxes and owls to see her, just as my fur makes it harder for mountain lions to spot me in the forest.

A notice

B place

C report

D mark

30 What does the prefix *un-* in *unnoticed* mean?

F very

G not

H little

J before

31 Water *evaporates* from your skin. The word *evaporates* means

A changes to ice.

B changes to a gas.

C drips off.

D sinks in.

32 You can be one *foot* away from a walking stick and never know it's there. In this sentence, what does *foot* mean?

F the bottom of a hill

G a measure of length

H the end part of a leg

J the end of a table

PART 3: WRITING CONVENTIONS

Directions

Mark your answer choice for Numbers 33 through 40.

For Numbers 33 through 36, mark which word fits best in the sentence.

33 Why did John _____ the back porch?

   A sweeping

   B swept

   C sweep

   D sweeps

34 Serena _____ her shoulders.

   F shrugging

   G have shrugged

   H shrugged

   J shrug

35 Marc _____ the idea of moving to a new city.

   A does enjoying

   B have enjoyed

   C was enjoyed

   D is enjoying

36 Toni and Bette _____ friends.

   F is

   G was

   H are

   J am

37 Which sentence is written correctly?

   A John explores the room and finds his keys.

   B John exploring the room and find his keys.

   C John explore the room and find his keys.

   D John will explore the room and finding his keys.

38 **Which sentence is written correctly?**

F They spins the big wheel three times.

G They is spinning the big wheel three times.

H They spinned the big wheel three times.

J They have spun the big wheel three times.

39 **Which question is written correctly?**

A Will you please point out the correct answer?

B Will you please pointing out the correct answer?

C Will you please pointed out the correct answer?

D Will you please to point out the correct answer?

40 **Which sentence is written correctly?**

F She kick the football over the fence.

G We kicks the football over the fence.

H He kicks the football over the fence.

J They kicks the football over the fence.

PART 4: WRITING

PROMPT

Both "Snowflakes" and "Blending In" discuss how we see things. Think about a situation in which you learned to see or understand something in a new and different way. Write an essay comparing your understanding before and after you saw something in a new way.

CHECKLIST FOR WRITERS

_____ Did I think about a time when I learned to see something in a new way?

_____ Did I take notes comparing my way of seeing something before and after this change?

_____ Did I organize my writing in a logical way?

_____ Did I use words and details that clearly express my ideas?

_____ Do my sentences make sense?

_____ Did I check my sentences for proper grammar and punctuation?

_____ Did I check my spelling?

_____ Did I make sure my paper is the way I want readers to read it?

NAME _____ DATE _____

Scott Foresman
Benchmark Test
Unit 4
Puzzles and Mysteries

PEARSON

Glenview, Illinois
Boston, Massachusetts
Chandler, Arizona
Upper Saddle River, New Jersey

ISBN-13: 978-0-328-53747-1
ISBN-10:   0-328-53747-0

1 2 3 4 5 6 7 8 9 10 V011 19 18 17 16 15 14 13 12 11 10
CC1

ISBN-13: 978-0-328-53747-1
ISBN-10:   0-328-53747-0

PART 1: COMPREHENSION

*D**irections***
Read some information about two kinds of hawks. Then do Numbers 1 through 11.

Hawk Identification

It's not easy to tell hawks apart when they are flying overhead. Even the best bird-watchers can have trouble telling the difference between the sharp-shinned hawk and the Cooper's hawk because these birds are so similar. The feathers, or plumage, of these adult hawks are nearly the same. Do not forget that these birds will not sit still while you try to figure out which kind they are.

These two kinds of hawks are different in size. Unless they are sitting next to each other, though, it is hard to judge their sizes. Also, the size of males and females of each species varies. (Females are about one-third larger than males for both kinds of hawk.) Another thing to think about is the difference between young and adult birds. Adult hawks are bigger than young hawks. Their bodies are shaped differently too. Younger hawks often have shorter wings and longer tails than adults.

Young hawks and adult hawks have different kinds of feathers. The Cooper's hawk has a dark cap on its head. This might help you tell it from a sharp-shinned hawk. You cannot always see a flying bird's head, though. Even if you see the head, you might mistake it for a young sharp-shinned hawk.

Looking at the hawk's tail might help. The Cooper's hawk and the sharp-shinned hawk have different kinds of tails. The Cooper's hawk has a round tail. The sharp-shinned hawk's tail is narrow. These differences are hard to spot when the birds are sitting.

The two hawks act differently. Cooper's hawks like to travel alone. They hardly ever bother other birds. Sharp-shinned hawks travel in small groups of about six birds. They can be aggressive toward other birds. They sometimes even fight with other sharp-shinned hawks!

Do not feel bad if you cannot distinguish between these two birds. Even bird experts disagree on sightings. These hawks are among the hardest of all birds to tell apart. If you spend a lot of time in the field, you can identify Cooper's hawks and sharp-shinned hawks. When you can tell the difference, you are a true hawk-watcher.

1 **What is one important difference between Cooper's hawks and sharp-shinned hawks?**

A Cooper's hawks are easier to recognize than sharp-shinned hawks.

B Cooper's hawks are less social than sharp-shinned hawks.

C Cooper's hawks are much larger than sharp-shinned hawks.

D Cooper's hawks have shorter wings and tails than sharp-shinned hawks.

2 **Which is most helpful in telling a Cooper's hawk and a sharp-shinned hawk apart?**

F the shape of their tails

G the length of their tails

H the length of their wings

J the shape of their heads

3 **What is the main idea of the last paragraph?**

A People who want to know about hawks should read about them.

B Hawk-watchers should not feel bad.

C Telling these hawks apart takes a lot of bird-watching time.

D Bird experts often disagree on which hawk is which.

GO ON

4 According to this selection, a hawk-watcher who spends many hours in the field

    F has to get used to sitting in trees and on fences.

    G learns that Cooper's hawks and sharp-shinned hawks are exactly the same.

    H can learn to tell the difference between Cooper's hawks and sharp-shinned hawks.

    J can learn to judge the size of the hawks.

5 It is hard to identify these hawks by their tails because their

    A tails look the same when the birds are sitting.

    B tails can't be seen when the birds are flying.

    C tails are often moving fast.

    D tail feathers are often missing.

6 What is true of both types of hawks?

    F The males have beautiful plumage.

    G The females are larger than the males.

    H They have the same color of head.

    J They are always ready to fight.

7 Other than size, the most important difference between young and old hawks is their

    A diet.

    B behavior.

    C beaks.

    D shape.

8 What situation would make it easiest to tell a Cooper's hawk from a sharp-shinned hawk?

    F looking at each hawk through a powerful telescope

    G comparing the young of each species as they sit in the nest

    H looking at flocks of each type of hawk as they fly together

    J studying an adult of each species as they sit in the same tree

9 The author's main purpose in writing this selection was to describe

    A the different lives of two kinds of hawks.

    B how difficult it can be to tell the age of a hawk.

    C why it is so hard to tell two kinds of hawks apart.

    D what it takes to become an expert bird-watcher.

10   Where should a sentence about the behavior of different hawks be added to this selection?

    F   paragraph one

    G   paragraph two

    H   paragraph four

    J   paragraph five

11   What is most important in becoming an expert on the difference between Cooper's and sharp-shinned hawks?

    A   observing young birds as they hatch and grow to adulthood

    B   observing the birds' appearances and behaviors over long periods of time

    C   observing male and female birds as they feed and care for their young

    D   observing the birds' aggressive behavior as they fight each other for food

GO ON

Directions
Write your answer to Question A on the lines below. Base your answer on "Hawk Identification."

A   Based on "Hawk Identification," what personal qualities would someone need in order to succeed in bird watching?

_____

_____

_____

_____

_____

_____

_____

_____

*D*irections

This story about a grandfather teaching his grandson the lessons of the hunt takes a different turn. Read the story. Then do Numbers 12 through 22.

The Hunt

It was early morning. Lopa went to the fire pit and stirred the ashes. Flames seemed to pop from nowhere, and he added some shavings of bark and strands of grass to the fire, so that he could boil some bark tea for his grandfather. This was the day his grandfather would take him to the forest and teach him to hunt.

Hours later, Lopa and his grandfather lay high on a bluff watching the riverbank for the game that would come there to drink. There could be deer or antelope, which were hard to sneak up on, or there might be wild pigs. There could also be muskrat and otter, or river ducks. But on this day, all they would do was see the animals, for they carried no weapons. Daka was a wise elder, and he knew that hunting was more about knowing the animals than taking them. He would have Lopa spend many days watching and learning. Whether they saw any game or not, they would talk long into the night about the day and what it meant.

Then Lopa heard it, and his body filled with excitement. He looked at his grandfather, but the elder's face showed no reaction. Lopa listened some more to a sound that started and stopped, sounding like branches scraping overhead, but it came from the river. It grew louder.

GO ON

Then around the bend swam two large creatures with arms longer than a man is tall, reaching out and pushing through the water. The noise was coming from their arms.

Lopa looked at Daka, but the old man said nothing.

Soon Lopa could see that the creatures were canoes, but not small and swift like those of his people. These were large and slow. They rode low in the water, and they carried eight men or more.

They steered into the bank underneath Lopa and Daka and started taking things from the canoes. They had many boxes and bags. Many had long sticks that they kept with them at all times. The men's bodies were covered with thick, heavy clothing, and it seemed to take them forever to make a camp.

That night when Lopa and his grandfather should have been talking about the animals they had seen, they had nothing to say. They had seen no animals.

Finally, the flames dropped down into the ashes and Lopa asked, "What were those men? What does it mean to have them in our river?"

The elder looked at his grandson and said, "I do not know. We will have to watch and talk and learn together."

12 **Why did the author include the campfire scene in the first paragraph?**

   F   to tell what was most important to Lopa

   G   to show how Lopa's important day began

   H   to explain how to get a fire started again

   J   to show how nervous Lopa was on this day

13 **Which words best describe most of Daka's teaching in "The Hunt"?**

   A   waiting and watching

   B   walking and talking

   C   thinking and acting

   D   listening and practicing

14 **How did the hunt described in paragraph two differ from the hunts Lopa would most likely go on when he grew older?**

   F   Lopa and his grandfather did not need food.

   G   Lopa and his grandfather were not very excited.

   H   Lopa and his grandfather failed to catch any animals.

   J   Lopa and his grandfather had no weapons.

15 Based on the selection, what was the grandfather trying to teach Lopa?

   A to move quietly and stay hidden

   B to survive alone in the wilderness

   C to learn the habits of animals

   D to care about other societies

16 In the third paragraph, what caused the scraping sound that made Lopa excited?

   F animals running near the river

   G men paddling in canoes

   H Daka adding wood to the fire

   J deer passing through trees

17 Which was the most likely reason Lopa and his grandfather saw no animals?

   A They were too busy talking about these strangers.

   B There were no animals in the area that day.

   C They were not hunting that day, only looking.

   D The animals were scared off by the strangers.

18 Based on paragraphs six and seven, what did Lopa and Daka consider most important about the strangers?

   F The strangers had canoes that were better than Lopa and Daka's.

   G The strangers brought things Lopa and Daka had never seen before.

   H The strangers disliked nature.

   J The strangers were not at all friendly.

19 When Lopa and Daka first heard something coming their way, how did their actions differ?

   A Lopa was less nervous.

   B Daka was more excited.

   C Lopa was less eager.

   D Daka was calmer.

GO ON

20 Why were Lopa and Daka able to watch the strangers without being seen by them?

   F   They were high above the strangers.

   G   They were hiding behind trees.

   H   They were hiding near the riverbank.

   J   They were talking very quietly.

21 What was the author trying to show with the following words: "the flames dropped down into the ashes"?

   A   The fire had lost its importance.

   B   Lopa would soon be falling asleep.

   C   A lot of time had passed.

   D   It was time for Lopa to make more tea.

22 What caused Lopa and Daka to be silent in the eighth paragraph?

   F   They heard animals moving around in the distance.

   G   They were listening for sounds made by the strangers.

   H   They were too tired to talk about hunting.

   J   They were thinking about the strangers.

Directions

Write your answer to Question B on the lines below. Base your answer on the two selections you have read.

B Think about the selections "Hawk Identification" and "The Hunt." Describe how they are similar and how they are different. Include details from each selection.

WRITING ACROSS TEXTS

_____

_____

_____

_____

_____

_____

_____

_____

_____

_____

_____

PART 2: VOCABULARY

Directions

Mark your answer choice for Numbers 23 through 32.

23 He added some shavings of bark and *strands* of grass to the fire. What is another word for *strands*?

  A piles

  B hairs

  C clumps

  D blades

24 Lopa and his grandfather lay high on a *bluff* watching the riverbank. What is another word for *bluff*?

  F cliff

  G beach

  H tower

  J branch

25 As Lopa watched the river, a sound grew *louder*. Which word means the opposite of *louder*?

  A bigger

  B higher

  C quieter

  D noisier

26 Lopa and his grandfather lay watching for the *game* that would come there to drink. In this sentence, *game* means

  F play.

  G contest.

  H plan.

  J animals.

27 The Cooper's hawk and the sharp-shinned hawk are very *similar*. Which word means the opposite of *similar*?

  A alike

  B different

  C usual

  D difficult

28 Sharp-shinned hawks can be *aggressive* toward other birds. Which word means the opposite of *aggressive*?

  F surprising

  G forceful

  H outgoing

  J gentle

29 Adult hawks are *obviously* bigger than young hawks. Which phrase could best replace the word *obviously*?

  A of course

  B at times

  C considered to be

  D by a large amount

30 Even bird *experts* disagree on sightings. Which word means the opposite of *experts*?

  F professionals

  G students

  H citizens

  J amateurs

31 The feathers, or *plumage*, of these adult hawks are nearly the same. What does *plumage* mean in this sentence?

  A wings of a hawk

  B size of a hawk

  C colors of a bird

  D feathers of a bird

32 Do not feel bad if you cannot *distinguish* between these two birds. The word *distinguish* in this sentence means

  F honor.

  G locate.

  H tell apart.

  J communicate with.

PART 3: WRITING CONVENTIONS

Directions

Mark your answer choice for Numbers 33 through 40.

For Numbers 33 through 37, mark the answer choice that correctly completes the sentence.

33 Mrs. Thompson asked _____ to rake her yard.

A Joe and me

B Joe and I

C me and him

D I and him

34 After she had spent three weeks with the Smiths, Sarah liked living with _____.

F his

G they

H he

J them

35 _____ went to the store.

A Me and her

B She and I

C They and me

D Her and I

36 Is _____ going with me?

F her

G he

H they

J you

37 Alice is someone _____ has trouble making up her mind.

A who

B she

C which

D whom

38 **Which sentence is written correctly?**

    F   When it's hot outside, do your babies cry?

    G   When its hot outside, do you're babies cry?

    H   When it's hot outside, do you're babies cry?

    J   When its hot outside, do your babies cry?

39 **Which sentence is written correctly?**

    A   Todd and Jay had mud on his shoes.

    B   Todd and Jay had mud on its shoes.

    C   Todd and Jay had mud on theirs shoes.

    D   Todd and Jay had mud on their shoes.

40 **Which sentence is written correctly?**

    F   She and I was happy.

    G   They was happy.

    H   She were happy.

    J   They were happy.

PART 4: WRITING

PROMPT

You may have heard someone say that "experience is the best teacher." Think about a time when you learned something new through experience. Write a story about what you learned and how you learned it.

CHECKLIST FOR WRITERS

_____ Did I think about a time I learned something new through experience?

_____ Did I take notes about what I did to learn the new thing?

_____ Did I tell my story in the correct order?

_____ Did I use words and details that clearly express my ideas?

_____ Do my sentences make sense?

_____ Did I check my sentences for proper grammar and punctuation?

_____ Did I check my spelling?

_____ Did I make sure my paper is the way I want readers to read it?

NAME _____   DATE _____

Scott Foresman

Benchmark Test

Unit 5
Adventures by Land, Air, and Water

Glenview, Illinois
Boston, Massachusetts
Chandler, Arizona
Upper Saddle River, New Jersey

ISBN-13: 978-0-328-53748-8
ISBN-10:   0-328-53748-9

1 2 3 4 5 6 7 8 9 10 V011 19 18 17 16 15 14 13 12 11 10
CC1

ISBN-13: 978-0-328-53748-8
ISBN-10:   0-328-53748-9

PART 1: COMPREHENSION

Directions

A pioneering family faced the challenges of building a new home and settling in. Read about the sod house they built and how they helped other newcomers. Then do Numbers 1 through 11.

A New Start

After a long and difficult journey from the East Coast, Sarah's family stopped in the Great Plains. This is where they would settle and begin their new life. While everyone was happy to stop traveling, they realized they faced many challenges.

Other families had arrived before Sarah's, and these settlers had built their homes along the rivers and streams. There was no more room for Sarah's family to build a house close to the water. The plains were covered with beautiful tall grasses, but there were very few trees. Sarah wondered how her father could build a house without wood. After talking to some of their neighbors, Sarah learned that the summers were very hot, while the winters were very cold. How would they stay comfortable in such a place?

Sarah's father began by building a windmill. He explained that it would pump water from underground. This way, the family would not have to walk to the stream and carry water back up to their house each day.

Sarah quickly learned how to build a house without timber. She and her mother cut strips of sod. The soil was held together by long grass roots. It was tough and flexible. They piled the sod strips one on top of the other, creating walls. The house would only have one door and two small windows, so very little timber would be needed. Sarah was relieved to learn that the sod walls would keep the house cool during the summer months and warm during the winter.

Sarah was in charge of the cows. She didn't know how to keep the livestock close by and safe. Her parents collected thorny brush from along the riverbanks. They piled the plants high and tied them together. This formed a rough enclosure that would work as a pen.

As Sarah and her parents continued to work on their new home, another family arrived in the area. They would have to settle even farther away from the river. There was not enough timber to build another windmill. Sarah and her parents welcomed their new neighbors and offered to share their water. As Sarah's mother explained, life was already difficult and unpredictable enough. The least they could do was to offer help to one another.

In return, the new neighbors provided Sarah's family with fresh eggs from their chickens. In no time, a community formed, and families traded goods and friendships.

1 **Which of the following happened first?**

A   Sarah and her mother made sod walls.

B   Sarah's father built a windmill.

C   Sarah and her parents welcomed new neighbors.

D   Sarah's parents made a pen for the cows.

2 **Which is the most likely reason the author wrote this selection?**

F   to entertain the reader with an amusing story

G   to express feelings about the pioneers' challenges

H   to tell what life was like for pioneers

J   to present one young girl's life story

3 **Why is it important to the plot that Sarah's family could not build their home right by the stream?**

A   It explained how little wood there was.

B   It explained why they were so uncomfortable.

C   It explained why they moved from the East Coast.

D   It explained why the family built a windmill.

GO ON

4 Which words best describe Sarah as she helped to build her house?

    F complaining and weak

    G helpful and strong

    H hot and uncaring

    J quiet and sad

5 The construction of a cow pen out of thorny brush shows that Sarah's parents were

    A impatient.

    B hopeful.

    C practical.

    D timid.

6 What lesson did Sarah learn about survival on the Great Plains?

    F Houses must be next to a water supply.

    G Houses are strongest when made of wood.

    H People must help each other.

    J People need to care for themselves first.

7 What can you conclude about Sarah?

    A She is shy and well-mannered.

    B She must be encouraged to work.

    C She has many younger brothers and sisters.

    D She learned many new things moving west.

8 How were the conflicts in the selection resolved?

    F Sarah's family moved west.

    G A pen was built for the cows.

    H The new neighbors became friends.

    J People used what they had.

9 Which statement best expresses the theme of "A New Start"?

    A Life on the Great Plains was filled with adventure and hardship.

    B Moving to an unknown place like the Great Plains was not a good idea.

    C Water was of great importance to settlers of the Great Plains.

    D Many young children contributed to settling the Great Plains.

10 Which sentence provides background information for the action in "A New Start"?

F While everyone was happy to stop traveling, they realized they faced many challenges.

G The plains were covered with tall and beautiful grasses, but there were very few trees.

H As Sarah and her parents continued to work on their new home, another family arrived in the area.

J In no time, a community formed, and families traded goods and friendships.

11 What kind of roof would Sarah's house most likely have had?

A steep and covered with brush

B steep and covered with prairie grass

C almost flat and covered with boards

D almost flat and covered with sod

Directions

Write your answer to Question A on the lines below. Base your answer on "A New Start."

A   Think about how the characters in "A New Start" helped one another. How does helping in the story compare to the way people help each other where you live?

_____

_____

_____

_____

_____

_____

_____

_____

_____

Directions

The Vine That Ate the South

Kudzu is a fast-growing vine that covers millions of acres in the southern United States. It is so common in that part of the country that one might think it is a native plant, but it is not. Kudzu was brought to the United States from Japan in 1876. Many Americans thought it was beautiful, and they began planting it. Little did they know it could grow up to a foot a day during the summer months. Nor did they know that it would grow up and over anything in its path.

In its native Japan, kudzu grew in a climate that included moderate winters and a short growing season. In the United States, southern weather is warm and wet, with short, mild winters and a very long growing season. The new climate was perfect for kudzu.

In the 1920s, people used the vine to feed farm animals. Ten years later, the government supported its use because it kept soil from washing away. However, by the 1950s, the government no longer wanted people to plant the vine. Twenty years after that, the government labeled it a harmful weed.

The vine grows up trees, light posts, and buildings, sometimes making beautiful shapes. However, it can also damage its surroundings. Trees die after kudzu covers

GO ON

them because they can't get enough light. Kudzu also can uproot trees because of its weight. Scientists looking for ways to kill the vine found that it is a very tough plant. Some of the poisons they used to try to kill it made it grow better. Kudzu roots are large and heavy, making them difficult to dig up.

Because kudzu is so hard to get rid of, some people are making the best of it by finding different uses for the vine. Some people put goats on land covered by kudzu. The vine feeds the goats, and the people sell the goat's milk and wool. Kudzu can be eaten by people, and it can be used to make paper and baskets. It is also being studied in the hope that it can be used as medicine. At the very least, kudzu serves as an example of the unexpected results that can occur from importing non-native plants.

12 **Which of the following happened first?**

F Kudzu's medicinal value was studied.

G The government claimed that kudzu was a weed.

H Kudzu was brought to the United States.

J The government encouraged people to plant kudzu.

13 **What is the most likely reason the author titled the selection "The Vine That Ate the South"?**

A to let readers know that kudzu is a vine

B to convince the reader that the selection is serious

C to let readers know the plant is dangerous

D to interest the reader with humor

14 **Why does kudzu cover everything in its path?**

F It is a climbing vine that grows very quickly.

G It has a short growing season in Japan.

H It is a plant that is difficult to kill.

J It has large and heavy roots.

15 **What is the last paragraph mostly about?**

A why people want to kill the vine

B how people use the vine

C how quickly the vine grows

D why people use the vine

16 What is the most likely reason the author wrote this article?

   F to persuade people not to plant more kudzu

   G to entertain people with jokes about kudzu

   H to inform people about where to buy kudzu

   J to inform people about the kudzu plant

17 Which of the following would be most useful in proving the fact that kudzu was brought to the United States in 1876?

   A atlas

   B dictionary

   C encyclopedia

   D almanac

18 What would happen to kudzu if the weather in the South stayed dry and cold all the time?

   F It would grow faster.

   G It would be easier to dig up.

   H It would kill more trees.

   J It would probably die.

19 What conclusion can you draw about importing non-native plants?

   A It is not allowed.

   B It helps the environment.

   C It can cause problems.

   D It is good to grow new plants.

20 Which statement is used by the author to support the claim that kudzu can damage its surroundings?

   F Kudzu was brought to the United States from Japan.

   G People used kudzu to feed animals.

   H Kudzu was used to keep soil from washing away.

   J The government labeled kudzu a harmful weed.

GO ON

21 The title of the selection is "The Vine That Ate the South." Which of the following would be best as another title?

A "Japanese Plants"

B "The Foot-a-Day Vine"

C "Why Climate Is Important"

D "Plants That Kill"

22 What is the author's main purpose for writing this selection?

F to teach the history of kudzu in the United States

G to explain how kudzu is used to make money

H to explain how scientists can use kudzu

J to tell where kudzu is from

Directions

Write your answer to Question B on the lines below. Base your answer on the two selections you have read.

B Both "A New Start" and "The Vine That Ate the South" tell about problems that people face. Give one example of a solution to a problem from each selection.

WRITING ACROSS TEXTS

_____

_____

_____

_____

_____

_____

_____

_____

_____

_____

_____

PART 2: VOCABULARY

Directions
Mark your answer choice for Numbers 23 through 32.

23 Sarah's parents collected thorny *brush* from along the riverbanks. What is the meaning of the homograph *brush* in this sentence?

   A   shrubs, bushes, and small trees

   B   a tool with bristles used for cleaning, sweeping, or painting

   C   a thinly settled country

   D   the bushy tail of an animal such as a fox

24 This is where the settlers would settle and *begin* their new life. Which of the following is a synonym for *begin?*

   F   realize

   G   imagine

   H   start

   J   continue

25 These settlers had built their homes along the rivers and *streams*. Which of the following is a synonym for *streams?*

   A   lakes

   B   shores

   C   ponds

   D   creeks

26 Which of the following is a pair of synonyms used in "A New Start"?

   F   relieved—provided

   G   windmill—water

   H   wood—timber

   J   close—safe

27 "The Vine That Ate the South" says that kudzu roots are *difficult* to dig up because they are large and heavy. What is another word for *difficult* as it is used in this sentence?

   A   simple

   B   hard

   C   tiresome

   D   effortless

28 Plants formed a rough enclosure to act as a *pen* for animals. What is the meaning of the homograph *pen* in this sentence?

F internal shell of a squid

G prison

H small, closed yard

J instrument used for writing or drawing with ink

29 Kudzu serves as an example of *unexpected* results. What is a synonym of the word *unexpected*?

A untried

B puzzling

C wonderful

D unplanned

30 However, kudzu can also damage its *surroundings*. What does *surroundings* mean?

F what is around something

G anything with a round shape

H any plants that grow around trees

J what was there before something else arrived

31 Kudzu also can *uproot* trees because of its weight. What is the meaning of *uproot* in this sentence?

A makes the trees' roots get stronger with age

B makes the trees' roots come out of the ground

C makes the trees' roots grow taller

D makes the trees' roots push the tree up higher

32 Which of the following is a pair of synonyms?

F milk—wool

G harmful—safe

H log—fire

J earth—soil

PART 3: WRITING CONVENTIONS

Directions

Mark your answer choice for Numbers 33 through 40.

33 **Which sentence is written correctly?**

    A   The loudly dogs kept us awake.

    B   She ran home rapid.

    C   Jane cheered happily for her sister.

    D   He tossed the ball careless at the window.

34 **Which sentence is written correctly?**

    F   We are exciting about the party.

    G   She was a cautiously swimmer.

    H   Lynn drew a elephant and colored it.

    J   All of my sisters are athletic.

35 **Which sentence is written correctly?**

    A   Tina is the smartest girl in my class.

    B   This towel is the more drier.

    C   That pillow is soft than this one.

    D   She is the gracefullest dancer.

36 **Read the following sentence:**

He read the directions <u>carefully</u>.

What part of speech is the underlined word?

    F   preposition

    G   adjective

    H   verb

    J   adverb

37 Read the following sentence:

The rusty bicycle is outside.

What part of speech is the underlined word?

A preposition

B adjective

C noun

D adverb

38 Which sentence is written correctly?

F He ate quick.

G Fran jumps highest than Todd.

H She sang sweetly.

J The bell rang long today than yesterday.

39 Read the following sentence:

The cat crawled into the box.

What part of speech is the underlined word?

A preposition

B adjective

C noun

D adverb

40 Read the following sentence:

She chased him around the tree.

Which of the following describes the underlined group of words?

F complete subject

G complete predicate

H prepositional phrase

J noun phrase

PART 4: WRITING

PROMPT

Both "A New Start" and "The Vine That Ate the South" tell about problems and how people deal with them. Think about a problem you would like to see solved. Write an essay that will convince the students in your class that the problem needs to be solved and that your solution will work.

CHECKLIST FOR WRITERS

_____ Did I think about a problem and how it should be solved?

_____ Did I take notes about the way I think the problem should be solved?

_____ Did I organize my writing in a logical way?

_____ Did I use words and details that clearly express my ideas?

_____ Do my sentences make sense?

_____ Did I check my sentences for proper grammar and punctuation?

_____ Did I check my spelling?

_____ Did I make sure my paper is the way I want readers to read it?

NAME _____   DATE _____

Scott Foresman
Benchmark Test
Unit 6
Reaching for Goals

PEARSON

Glenview, Illinois
Boston, Massachusetts
Chandler, Arizona
Upper Saddle River, New Jersey

ISBN-13: 978-0-328-53749-5
ISBN-10:   0-328-53749-7

1 2 3 4 5 6 7 8 9 10 V011 19 18 17 16 15 14 13 12 11 10
CC1

ISBN-13: 978-0-328-53749-5
ISBN-10:   0-328-53749-7

PART 1: COMPREHENSION

Directions
Read this selection about recycling plastic. Then do Numbers 1 through 11.

From Trash to Treasure

How are park benches, pencils, carpet, and certain pieces of clothing alike? Plastic can be used to produce all of these. If a plastic bottle is thrown away and it ends up in a landfill, it will take up space for a long time. It will not break down for hundreds of years! It is better to turn our trash into things that can be used.

Have you ever noticed the numbers on the bottom of a plastic bottle? These numbers tell what type of plastic was used to make the bottle. It's hard to believe, but a soft-drink bottle with the number one on the bottom can be used to make a soft, fuzzy, warm fabric called fleece. This light and strong cloth can keep you as warm as wool can, but if it gets wet, it will dry much faster than wool. The fleece produced from the plastic is made into jackets, blankets, and even pet beds.

So how does plastic become clothing? The first step is for the plastic to be taken to a recycling center. There are bins at the center that have numbers on them. The number on the bottom of the bottles should match the number on the bin. It is important to have all of the same types of plastics together. All the things that have been dropped off at the recycling center are then taken to a bigger center. Here, they are sorted again. Next, the bottles are cleaned and chopped into tiny pieces. These pieces are melted. Then the melted material is forced through tiny holes in flat plates. This makes long, thin strands. After these become hard, they are spun into long threads. The threads are then stretched. The threads are also wrinkled so that they will have the small curls or waves that natural threads and fibers have. These threads are then woven into cloth. The cloth is made into clothing, blankets, and pet beds. It takes about twenty-five 2-liter bottles to make one fleece jacket. Making treasures out of trash—now that's special!

1   **Look at the picture. Which of the following can be recycled there?**

  A   rubber

  B   wire

  C   cloth

  D   glass

2   **Which of the following is a statement of opinion?**

  F   It is better to turn our trash into things that can be used.

  G   There are bins at the recycling center that have numbers on them.

  H   The bottles are cleaned and chopped into tiny pieces.

  J   It takes about twenty-five 2-liter bottles to make one fleece jacket.

3   **Based on the picture, you can tell that**

  A   wood is recycled here.

  B   metal is recycled here.

  C   there are two different kinds of plastic.

  D   there are five different kinds of glass.

GO ON

4 What resource could you use to check the fact that plastic does not break down easily?

F dictionary

G almanac

H thesaurus

J encyclopedia

5 Some park benches and pencils are alike in that they both can be

A made from plastic.

B turned into different products.

C turned into fleece cloth.

D found at recycling centers.

6 What is one disadvantage of putting plastics in landfills?

F The plastic rots away too quickly.

G The world could run out of plastic.

H The plastic that could be used again is wasted.

J The water supply could become unsafe.

7 How are numbers on the bottom of plastic bottles used?

A to make sorting for recycling easier

B to show how strong the plastic is

C to let people know how much the bottles cost

D to let companies keep up with how many bottles they made

8 When using plastic to make clothing, what happens after the threads are wrinkled?

F They are melted.

G They are made into cloth.

H They are stretched.

J They are cleaned and chopped.

9 The title of the selection is "From Trash to Treasure." Which would be another good title?

A "How Plastic Is Made"

B "The History of Recycling"

C "Why Fleece Was Invented"

D "Making Old Plastic New Again"

10 What was probably the author's main purpose for writing this selection?

F to explain how to recycle

G to entertain readers

H to explain how plastic is made into new things

J to convince readers to recycle their trash

11 What is done to the threads of plastic to make them more like natural threads?

A They are melted.

B They are wrinkled.

C They are spun.

D They are cleaned.

Directions

Write your answer to Question A on the lines below. Base your answer on "From Trash to Treasure."

A   Give at least one example of why recycling is a good idea. Use details from the selection to explain your answer.

_____

_____

_____

_____

_____

_____

_____

_____

_____

Directions
Harriet Tubman led many people out of slavery to freedom. Read about her life.
Then do Numbers 12 through 22.

Harriet Tubman: Making a Difference

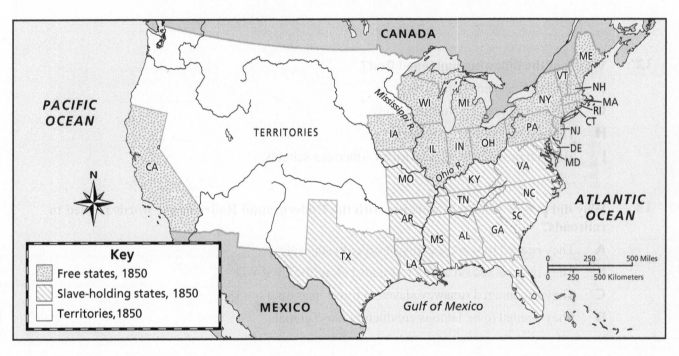

Key
- Free states, 1850
- Slave-holding states, 1850
- Territories, 1850

Harriet Tubman was born into slavery in Maryland sometime around 1820. At a young age she suffered a serious head injury on the plantation where she lived and worked as a slave. For the rest of her life, this injury would cause her to faint suddenly.

Tubman escaped from Maryland in 1849, traveling north to the "free states" where slavery was not allowed. Other people probably would have forgotten about their past and started a new life. But Tubman did not turn her back on others who needed help. She returned many times to states that allowed slavery so that she could help other people reach freedom in the North, just as she had done. She became one of the best-known conductors on the Underground Railroad.

The Underground Railroad was not really under the ground, nor was it actually a railroad. It was a secret network of hidden paths and sympathetic homeowners who helped runaway slaves travel to freedom. The homes where the runaways stopped along the way were called stations. The people who helped them were called conductors. The runaway slaves themselves were referred to as packages or freight. By using these words, the conductors were able to keep others from finding

GO ON

out about their actions.

Tubman risked her life for her beliefs, not once, but over and over again. She was able to lead her own parents to freedom, as well as many of her brothers and sisters. She also served as a nurse, a scout, and a spy for the Northern army during the Civil War. She went into the Southern army's territory, collecting information that was needed by the North. She was a brave woman who used her wits to outsmart her enemies.

Even after the Civil War ended and slavery was illegal in all states, Tubman continued to help other people. She raised money for schools for the newly freed African Americans. She had a home built for African Americans who were poor or sick. Tubman herself spent the last two years of her life there.

12   **Which of the following happened first?**

   F   Tubman escaped from slavery.

   G   Tubman helped the Northern army.

   H   Tubman suffered a head injury.

   J   Tubman raised money for African American schools.

13   **Why did people who were working with the Underground Railroad use words related to railroads?**

   A   They needed to work secretly in order to stay safe.

   B   They had worked on actual railroads before the Civil War.

   C   They encouraged runaway slaves to travel near train tracks.

   D   They wanted to be famous conductors like Tubman.

14   **What is the third paragraph mostly about?**

   F   where the Underground Railroad was located

   G   when the Underground Railroad started

   H   why the Underground Railroad was started

   J   how the Underground Railroad worked

15 **Which of the following is a statement of opinion?**

    A   Other people probably would have forgotten about their past and started a new life.

    B   She became one of the best-known conductors on the Underground Railroad.

    C   Tubman risked her life for her beliefs, not once, but over and over again.

    D   Even after the Civil War ended, Tubman continued to help other people.

16 **Based on the selection, which word best describes Harriet Tubman?**

    F   wealthy

    G   mysterious

    H   courageous

    J   popular

17 **Look at the map. Which two free states are closest to Maryland?**

    A   Ohio and Indiana

    B   Pennsylvania and New Jersey

    C   Virginia and Kentucky

    D   Connecticut and Massachusetts

18 **What was the author's main purpose for writing this selection?**

    F   to entertain the reader with a good story

    G   to teach about a secret railroad

    H   to express feelings about the Civil War

    J   to tell the reader about Tubman's life

19 **Which of the following is a statement of opinion?**

    A   Harriet Tubman was born in Maryland sometime around 1820.

    B   The Underground Railroad was a secret network to help runaway slaves reach freedom.

    C   She was able to lead her own parents to freedom.

    D   She was a brave woman who used her wits to fool her enemies.

20 Which of these resources could be used to check the following statement of fact?

> *She also served as a nurse, a scout, and a spy for the Northern army during the Civil War.*

F atlas

G almanac

H biography

J dictionary

For Numbers 21 and 22, look at the map on page 7.

21 After Tubman escaped from Maryland (MD), she settled in New York (NY). What is the most likely reason she didn't settle in a free state closer to Maryland?

A The weather in New York was better.

B She wanted to decrease the chance of being captured.

C The Underground Railroad led to New York.

D She wanted to join family members who had already escaped.

22 What is the fewest number of slave states a runaway slave from Alabama (AL) would have had to go through to get to a free state in the North?

F one

G two

H four

J five

Directions

Write your answer to Question B on the lines below. Base your answer on the two selections you have read.

B Think about the theme of making things better in "From Trash to Treasure" and "Harriet Tubman." Write one fact from each selection that supports the theme of making things better.

WRITING ACROSS TEXTS

_____

_____

_____

_____

_____

_____

_____

_____

_____

PART 2: VOCABULARY

Directions
Mark your answer choice for Numbers 23 through 32.

23 Tubman suffered a serious head injury on the *plantation* where she lived. Which of the following is the root word of *plantation*?

A plant

B plan

C ant

D land

24 Which meaning of *produce* is used in this sentence?

Plastic can be used to produce all of these.

F vegetables

G bear

H grow

J make

25 All the things that have been dropped off at the *recycling* center are then taken to a bigger center. Which of the following is the root word of *recycling*?

A cling

B cycle

C cycling

D bicycle

26 Which meaning of *center* is used in this sentence?

The first step is for the plastic to be taken to a recycling center.

F the middle point of a circle

G a place people go to for a particular purpose

H halfway between the ends

J a player with the middle position on a team

27 Which meaning of *space* is used in this sentence?

It will take up space for a long time.

A the area in which the universe exists

B an area of ground

C where to park a car

D a period of time

28 What are the guide words for the page in the dictionary on which the word *strands* is found?

F stream—sword

G standardize—statesman

H stretch—stew

J storybook—straw

Use this entry from a dictionary to answer Numbers 29 through 31.

> **rest** (rest), **1** *n.* state of quiet and ease; sleep: *a good night's rest.* **2** *v.* to be still or quiet; sleep: *Lie down and rest.* **3** *n.* time of ease and freedom from activity or trouble: *I left the swimming pool for a short rest.* **4** *v.* to place or be placed for support; lay; lean: *He rested his rake against the fence.* **5** *n.* what is left: *The sun was out in the morning, but it rained for the rest of the day.* **6** *v.* to continue to be; remain: *The final decision rests with you.*

29 According to the dictionary entry, the word *rest* can be used as which two parts of speech?

A noun and adjective

B adverb and verb

C noun and verb

D adjective and preposition

30 Which dictionary meaning of *rest* is used in this sentence?

For the rest of her life, this injury would cause her to faint suddenly.

F definition 2

G definition 3

H definition 4

J definition 5

GO ON

31 What is the dictionary meaning for *rested* as used in this sentence?

The man's stare rested on the beautiful painting.

A slept

B remained

C left

D leaned

32 What are the guide words for the page in the dictionary on which the word *actually* is found?

F aboveboard—accident

G accidental—acidity

H acknowledge—acting

J action—address

PART 3: WRITING CONVENTIONS

Directions

Mark your answer choice for Numbers 33 through 40.

33 **Which sentence is written correctly?**

  A   The man asked "us to be quiet."

  B   "What time is dinner?" she asked.

  C   He said, I'm ready to go.

  D   "Let's plant a garden, she said."

34 **Which sentence is written correctly?**

  F   We saw cows horses, and pigs.

  G   What's so funny Rosa?

  H   Mom bought grapes, apples and, berries.

  J   Yes, I guess I should go now.

35 **Which sentence is written correctly?**

  A   She lives on Dover street.

  B   My aunt lives in texas.

  C   He's a member of the Roseville Club.

  D   I wrote a letter to uncle Dave.

36 **Which sentence is written correctly?**

  F   Dorene, will you help me please?

  G   We washed rinsed and dried the dishes.

  H   Her dog likes to bark, and run.

  J   My cousin moved to Atlanta Georgia.

37 **Which sentence is written correctly?**

  A   My favorite story is Banana Boy.

  B   The teacher told the class "to go home."

  C   I love to read, she said.

  D   She wrote a story called "Amelia's Adventures."

38 Read the following sentences:

It was raining. We went outside anyway.

Which sentence combines the two sentences correctly?

F It was raining, but we went outside anyway.

G It was raining outside anyway.

H It was raining or we went outside anyway.

J It was raining, we went outside anyway.

39 Read the following sentences:

Tony took a book off the shelf. He began to read.

Which sentence best combines the two sentences into one?

A Beginning to read, Tony took a book off the shelf.

B Tony took it off the shelf, and then he began to read.

C Taking a book off the shelf, Tony he began to read.

D Tony took a book off the shelf and began to read.

40 Choose the word that should begin with a capital letter in this sentence.

My mom saw mister Smith at the grocery store.

F mom

G mister

H grocery

J store

16

PART 4: WRITING

PROMPT

Both "From Trash to Treasure" and "Harriet Tubman: Making a Difference" tell about changing things to make them better. Think about a time that you worked to make something better. Write an essay that describes what you made better. Be sure to describe the thing you changed both before and after the change.

CHECKLIST FOR WRITERS

_____ Did I think about a time that I made something better?

_____ Did I list details about what I changed both before and after the change?

_____ Did I organize my paper in a logical way?

_____ Did I use words and details that clearly describe the change?

_____ Do my sentences make sense?

_____ Did I check my sentences for proper grammar and punctuation?

_____ Did I check my spelling?

_____ Did I make sure my paper is the way I want readers to read it?

NAME _____ DATE _____

Scott Foresman
Benchmark Test
End-of-Year

PEARSON

Glenview, Illinois
Boston, Massachusetts
Chandler, Arizona
Upper Saddle River, New Jersey

ISBN-13: 978-0-328-53750-1
ISBN-10:   0-328-53750-0

ISBN-13: 978-0-328-53750-1
ISBN-10:   0-328-53750-0

1 2 3 4 5 6 7 8 9 10 V011 19 18 17 16 15 14 13 12 11 10
CC1

Directions

The English alphabet is only one of several alphabets in existence. Read about *hangul*, the Korean alphabet. Then do Numbers 1 through 11.

Sejong the Great

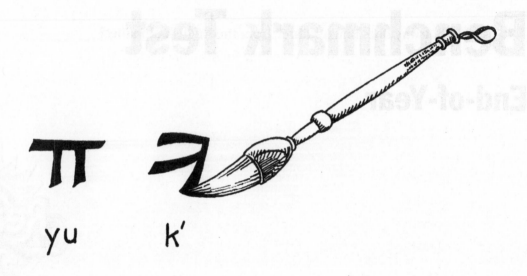

Many years ago, a king named Sejong ruled Korea. Sejong was the fourth king of the Yi dynasty, a family of kings and queens who ruled Korea for more than five hundred years. Born in 1397, Sejong was king of Korea for more than thirty years, from 1419 until he died in 1450. During his rule, Korea enjoyed many cultural changes in the arts, writing, and education.

Sejong is best known for the invention of the Korean alphabet, which is called *hangul*. The word *hangul* means "great script." It is an alphabet like the one we use in English. Letters in hangul stand for sounds that people make when they speak. In the Korean alphabet, there are twenty-four letters: fourteen consonants and ten vowels. In the English alphabet, there are twenty-six letters, five of which are vowels. The Korean alphabet has more vowels than English, but the English alphabet has more consonants.

In hangul, the consonants are written with curved or angled lines, and the vowels are written with straight vertical lines that go up and down or horizontal lines that go from side to side. Above are examples of a consonant and vowel in hangul.

In 1446, Sejong, who was known as Sejong the Great, declared that hangul would be the official writing system of Korea. However, Sejong found it difficult to make this change a reality because many people in Korea used the older

Chinese system of writing at the time. The large neighboring country of China had influenced the culture of Korea for a long time. Scholars and people from the upper classes did not want to change their writing habits, so many of them did not use hangul at first.

The Yi dynasty, to which Sejong belonged, ruled Korea from 1392 through 1910. Then Japan invaded Korea and took over the country. Japan ruled Korea until the end of World War II in 1945. After 1945, people once again began to use hangul widely in Korea, and the alphabet is used there to this day.

1 **In what way does hangul differ from the English alphabet?**

A   Hangul has more vowels than the English alphabet.

B   Hangul has more consonants than the English alphabet.

C   The English alphabet has vowels, but hangul does not.

D   Hangul has more letters than the English alphabet does.

2 **Which of the following words from the second paragraph is a clue to a comparison?**

F   invention

G   which

H   like

J   for

3 **Based on the third paragraph, the letter on the right side of the drawing is**

A   a vowel.

B   a consonant.

C   an English letter.

D   a Chinese character.

4 **Which of the following is a statement of opinion?**

F   Sejong ruled Korea for more than thirty years.

G   Sejong belonged to the Yi dynasty.

H   Sejong invented the Korean alphabet.

J   Sejong was a great ruler of Korea.

GO ON

5 What is the main idea of the fourth paragraph?

A Some scholars did not want to learn a new system of writing.

B People in Korea once used the Chinese system of writing.

C It was difficult to make hangul the official writing system of Korea.

D Hangul was declared the official writing system by Sejong.

6 The author probably wrote this selection to

F persuade the reader to learn the Korean alphabet.

G express an opinion about what is the best language.

H tell about the influence of a king on his country.

J entertain the reader with a lively story about Korea.

7 Why did it take so long for people to use hangul widely in Korea?

A People were used to a different system of writing.

B Sejong did not want scholars to use the new alphabet.

C Most people did not want to learn to write.

D There were few books being written for people to read.

8 According to the selection, which of the following events occurred last?

F Japan invaded Korea.

G People used hangul widely after 1945.

H Sejong died.

J Hangul was declared to be the official Korean alphabet.

9 Which of the following is a statement of fact?

A Sejong deserved to be called Sejong the Great.

B Sejong was the fourth king of the Yi dynasty.

C Hangul was Sejong's most important invention.

D China was a helpful neighbor during Sejong's rule.

10 Which fact below best supports the conclusion that Sejong was a great king?

F Sejong was a member of the Yi dynasty, which ruled Korea for five hundred years.

G Sejong found it difficult to get many people to use hangul.

H Sejong was the king of Korea for more than thirty years.

J Sejong invented the Korean system of writing.

11 **Why did people in Korea use the Chinese system of writing during Sejong's time?**

A China had invaded Korea in 1945.

B China had influenced Korea for a long time.

C China was a bigger country than Korea.

D Most Korean people went to school in China.

Reading can sometimes be a matter of understanding the code. Read the following selection about how two friends communicated in their own code. Then do Numbers 12 through 22.

The Secret Code

Lydia liked to talk to friends and play her tuba, but her favorite activity was reading. She read a lot. Sometimes her mother would find Lydia asleep on the couch with a book over her face. When that happened, her mother would gently remove the book and cover Lydia with a blanket.

Lydia's best friend, Avi, liked to read too, but not as much as Lydia did. He was more interested in working on the clubhouse his father and he had built together. Along one wall of the clubhouse, Avi had lined up a row of jars that contained various kinds of dried flowers. In the clubhouse Avi and Lydia sometimes discussed what they would be when they grew up. Avi thought he might study plants, and Lydia thought she would be a writer.

One rainy day when Lydia and Avi were walking toward the clubhouse, Lydia saw a folded note on the ground. She picked it up, but to her surprise she couldn't read it. The note was written in a strange language. Avi couldn't read the words either.

"I wonder if I can crack the code," said Lydia.

In the clubhouse Lydia read the note over and over. Finally, she figured out the message. "It says 'Thank you for the present,'" she told Avi. "Whoever wrote this just left off the first letter of each word."

"That was good thinking," said Avi.

"I'm going to write you a note in a language I invent," Lydia announced. "It will be our secret code."

Lydia took a pen and some paper from her backpack. She thought a few minutes, wrote something, and handed the paper to Avi. "Mio yhappo uyoo earo ymo dfrieno" were the words in the note.

At that moment Avi realized the sun was setting, which meant he had to go home for dinner. "I'll take your note with me," he told Lydia. "Maybe by tomorrow I'll crack your code."

Later that evening, as Avi was walking his dog, he suddenly grinned. He knew what the note said. When he got home, he wrote a note to Lydia in the same new language.

The next day in the clubhouse, Avi handed Lydia his note. She smiled and read it aloud. "Thanks, I'm happy you're my friend. And I like having a new language to write in."

Lydia and Avi agreed to use the new code whenever they wrote notes to each other. They even kept up the practice for a "ecouplo foo smontho."

12 **Why did Lydia have trouble reading the note she found on the ground?**

F The ink had been smeared by rain.

G The note was written in code.

H The note was torn up into pieces.

J There were too many folds in the paper.

13 **Why did Avi keep jars of dried flowers in the clubhouse?**

A He wanted to learn more about plants and flowers.

B His father told him to store the flowers.

C He was drying the flowers for his mother.

D He found a note telling him to collect dried flowers.

GO ON

14 How were Lydia and Avi different from each other?

F Lydia liked to read more than Avi did.

G Lydia wanted to study plants, but Avi did not.

H Avi wanted to be a writer, but Lydia wanted to be a tuba player.

J Avi wrote a note in a made-up language, but Lydia did not.

15 Which word from the fifth paragraph is a clue word showing sequence?

A over

B Finally

C hour

D told

16 The author probably wrote this story to

F persuade the reader to learn other languages.

G entertain the reader with a story about two children.

H describe how to build a clubhouse.

J show how new languages are invented.

17 Which of the following is the best statement of the story's theme?

A Language is just as important as science.

B Friends with different interests may find it difficult to get along.

C Education is the key to success.

D There is more than one way to communicate with friends.

18 Lydia's mother can best be described as

F quiet.

G clever.

H caring.

J confused.

19 What are the first and second paragraphs mostly about?

A what Lydia and Avi did whenever they were together

B how Avi and Lydia were different

C how Avi and Lydia spent their time in the clubhouse

D what Lydia and Avi wanted to be when they grew up

20 What happened in the story's resolution?

F Lydia's mother covered her when she fell asleep reading.

G Lydia figured out the note on the ground.

H Avi figured out the language Lydia invented.

J Lydia could not read the note she found by Avi's clubhouse.

21 Lydia can best be described as

A gentle.

B intelligent.

C shy.

D athletic.

22 Which of the following occurred last in the story?

F Lydia figured out the code used in the note she found.

G Lydia and Avi agreed to use the new code to write notes.

H Avi walked his dog after eating dinner with his family.

J Avi handed Lydia a note he had written.

Directions

Write your answer to Question A on the lines below. Base your answer on the two selections you have read.

A Think about the selections "Sejong the Great" and "The Secret Code." Describe how the selections are similar and how they are different. Include details from each selection.

_____

_____

_____

_____

_____

_____

_____

_____

_____

_____

_____

*D*irections

Going on a field trip can be fun, but preparation is necessary in advance. Read the following letter about one field trip. Then do Numbers 23 through 33.

Going to Tiger Mountain

Tiger Mountain Trails

N W E S

Waterfall

Start of trails

Wooden bridge

Elm Elementary School
100 Oak Street
Seattle, WA 98100
May 2, 20____

Dear Class:

Hello. I am writing to you and your parents to tell you about our upcoming field trip to Tiger Mountain. I'm sure you're all very excited about the trip. I know I am. The trip will take half a day. We plan to leave the school by 8 A.M. on Saturday, May 21, 20____. So far, twenty-two students have signed up for the trip. It is important for everyone to arrive on time so that there are no delays. I will also need all your permission slips signed a week before the day we leave.

The plan for the trip is simple: After arriving at Tiger Mountain, we will all hike to the top of the mountain. In addition to me, Ms. Gearen will be leading the trip. Several parents, including Mr. Hollander and Mr. Chickadel, will also accompany us to make sure that everything goes smoothly. Ms. Gearen has hiked

GO ON

the trail many times, and she estimates that it will take about three hours to do the hike, including a half-hour break to enjoy the great views and eat lunch at the summit.

Please remember to bring a sack lunch and plenty of water with you for the hike. I recommend that you pack a sandwich, some crackers or other snacks, a piece of fruit, and at least one liter of water. You should also bring the following items: a waterproof jacket, a cap to shield your face from the sun, a warm hat and gloves, an extra shirt, an extra pair of socks, and a small flashlight. As usual, you should wear comfortable hiking shoes or sneakers and comfortable clothing.

I know this sounds like a long list of items to bring, but we need to be prepared for any kind of weather. As you know, the day may start out sunny but end up raining. The adults will also be packing first-aid kits in case there is an emergency of some kind.

We will be taking the easy trail marked with dotted lines on the map. Along the way, we will probably see some birds and chipmunks, but don't worry—there is no chance of us running into tigers! Please study the map ahead of time so you know what to expect.

Thank you for being prepared for the trip. Your efforts will make the trip enjoyable and safe for everybody.

Sincerely,

Ms. Megan Ramírez

23 **Why did Ms. Ramírez write this letter?**

A to describe a place the children would visit

B to tell people the history of Tiger Mountain

C to help students and parents prepare for a trip

D to entertain people with a tale about a trip

24 **According to the letter, which will happen last?**

F lunch at the top of the mountain

G meet to start hiking on the easy trail

H turn in permission slips

J leave school at 8 A.M.

25 **Which word from the second paragraph is a clue word showing sequence?**

A plan

B After

C also

D including

26 Ms. Gearen is leading the hike because

F she is the head teacher.

G she is the fastest hiker.

H she is trained in first aid.

J she knows the trail well.

27 What is the main idea of the third paragraph?

A Students should protect themselves from rain and sun.

B Students should bring at least one liter of water.

C Students should wear comfortable hiking shoes or sneakers.

D Students should prepare for the trip by packing carefully.

28 Why did Ms. Ramírez ask students to bring a waterproof jacket?

F They are going canoeing.

G It may start to rain.

H They will be camping overnight.

J The weather might turn cold.

29 The title of the selection is "Going to Tiger Mountain." Which of the following would be best as another title?

A "In All Kinds of Weather"

B "Ms. Ramírez Goes on a Field Trip"

C "Getting Prepared to Have Fun"

D "Chipmunks and Birds, but No Tigers"

30 According to the trail map, the students on the trip will probably see a

F school.

G tiger.

H volcano.

J waterfall.

31 According to the map, the wooden bridge is in which direction from the start of trails?

A south

B north

C east

D west

GO ON

32 Which of the following is a statement of fact?

F So far, twenty-two students have signed up for the trip.

G I'm sure you're excited about the trip.

H The plan for the trip is simple.

J This journey will be very enjoyable for everyone.

33 Ms. Ramírez probably asked students to study the map ahead of time because

A they will not have maps at Tiger Mountain.

B there is only one map for everybody.

C they need to become familiar with the trail.

D they will have to take a test before they hike.

Write your answer to Question B on the lines below. Base your answer on "The Secret Code" and "Going to Tiger Mountain."

B In "The Secret Code" and "Going to Tiger Mountain," characters write notes or letters. Describe how the purposes of the notes in "The Secret Code" and the letter in "Going to Tiger Mountain" are different. Include details from each selection.

WRITING ACROSS TEXTS

_____

_____

_____

_____

_____

_____

_____

_____

_____

PART 2: VOCABULARY

Directions

Mark your answer choice for Numbers 34 through 48.

34 Japan *invaded* Korea in 1910 and took over the country. What does *invaded* mean?

F   shared

G   smiled

H   attacked

J   forgot

35 What does the prefix *re-* mean in the word *replace?*

A   again

B   under

C   next

D   not

36 Which meaning of *trip* is used in the following sentence?

The plan for the trip is simple: After arriving at Tiger Mountain, we will all hike to the top of the mountain.

F   a switch

G   a mistake

H   a fall

J   a journey

37 Which meaning of *row* is used in the following sentence?

Avi had lined up a row of jars along one wall that contained various kinds of dried flowers.

A   a noisy argument

B   things arranged in a line

C   a narrow street of houses

D   to move a boat across water

38 What does *realized* mean in the following sentence?

> At that moment Avi realized the sun was setting, which meant he had to go home for dinner.

F wanted

G knew

H ready

J allowed

39 The note was written in a *strange* language. Which of these is an antonym for *strange?*

A pretty

B happy

C difficult

D familiar

40 The word *hangul* means *"great* script." Which word below means the opposite of *great?*

F unpopular

G unimportant

H beautiful

J many

41 Which word could be used instead of the phrase *stand for* in the following sentence?

> Letters in hangul stand for sounds that people make when they speak.

A believe

B finish

C enter

D mean

42 The teacher suggested that students should wear *comfortable* hiking shoes. Which word has the same suffix as *comfortable?*

F enjoyable

G table

H vegetable

J fable

GO ON

43 Read the following sentences:

Here is what I suggest you carry. I recommend that you pack a sandwich, a piece of fruit, and at least one liter of water.

Which word in the sentences is a synonym for *recommend*?

A pack

B here

C suggest

D carry

44 What does *marked* mean in the following sentence?

We will be taking the easy trail marked with dotted lines on the map.

F colored

G checked

H hidden

J shown

45 What does *shield* mean in the following sentence?

You should also bring the following items: a waterproof jacket and a cap to shield your face from the sun.

A surround

B protect

C flat piece of armor

D badge

46 Read the following sentences:

Several parents will also be accompanying us. They are coming with us to make sure everything goes smoothly.

Which phrase in the second sentence is a synonym for *accompanying*?

F they are

G coming with

H make sure

J goes smoothly

Use this entry from a dictionary to answer Numbers 47 and 48.

> **change** (chānj), **1** *v.* to make or become different: *She changed the decoration of the room.* **2** *v.* to put on different clothes: *After swimming we went to the cabin and changed.* **3** *v.* to transfer from one aircraft, train, bus, etc., to another: *Passengers must change here for Chicago.* **4** *n.* coins of small denomination: *She was carrying a dollar and some change.*
> ☐ *v.* **changed, chang•ing**

47 According to the dictionary entry, the word *change* can be used as which two parts of speech?

A   noun and verb

B   adverb and verb

C   noun and adjective

D   adjective and preposition

48 What is the dictionary meaning for *change* as used in this sentence?

Scholars and people from the upper classes did not want to change their writing habits, so many of them did not use hangul at first.

F   definition 1

G   definition 2

H   definition 3

J   definition 4

PART 3: WRITING CONVENTIONS

Directions
Mark your answer choice for Numbers 49 through 60.

49 **Which of the following is an imperative sentence?**

A   I love this pie!

B   Please hand me the salsa.

C   Lucy lives in New York City.

D   When will it stop raining?

50 **Which sentence is written correctly?**

F   She clapped loudly at the concert.

G   The dog jumped rough on the door.

H   He smiled sweet at his mother.

J   The quietly children sat at the table.

51 **Which sentence is written correctly?**

A   He went camping in lost pines state park.

B   We visited my cousin in New York.

C   She invited coach Peter to the party.

D   Her new address is 434 Willow drive.

52 **Which sentence is written correctly?**

F   Ben liked to cook Katie did too.

G   If you feel tired you should rest?

H   When it is warm, we wear shorts.

J   Samir works on Monday but Ali does not.

53 **Which sentence is written correctly?**

A   Juan looked after the two baby's.

B   How many calfs are in the field?

C   Joshua is one of the boys in the band.

D   Matt bought four loafses of bread.

54 **Which sentence is written correctly?**

   F   The nurses' station is empty.

   G   The familys house is for sale.

   H   The mouse'ses nest is ready.

   J   The deers antlers are sharp.

55 **Which of the following sentences uses a linking verb?**

   A   We were good friends.

   B   Louise dances well.

   C   She opened the box.

   D   The dog barked loudly.

56 **Which of the following sentences uses the past tense correctly?**

   F   We have went to the opera.

   G   Karl has took photographs of the scene.

   H   She gone home in the evening.

   J   I wrote a note to him that morning.

57 **Which sentence is written correctly?**

   A   We is painting.

   B   You am sleeping.

   C   I was awake.

   D   They be singing.

58 **What does *it* refer to in the following sentence?**

Monica sealed the letter and mailed it to Eric.

   F   Monica

   G   sealed

   H   letter

   J   Eric

59 **Which sentence is written correctly?**

    A   Last July was hottest than the last one.

    B   It was the drier season in ten years.

    C   That person is most graceful than Sue.

    D   She did a better job than Sylvia.

60 **Which sentence is written correctly?**

    F   I packed a hat, some gloves, and a book.

    G   The carpet is, worn dirty and old.

    H   He wanted to eat bacon eggs, and potatoes.

    J   She swam biked and ran all summer, long.

PART 4: WRITING

PROMPT

"Going to Tiger Mountain" tells about an upcoming school hiking trip. Pretend your school is planning an outdoors program for students to learn how to hike and practice other outdoors skills.

Write a persuasive essay stating why an outdoors skills program would be a good idea or a bad idea. Give reasons to support your opinion.

CHECKLIST FOR WRITERS

_____ Did I think about whether an outdoors program would be a good idea for my school?

_____ Did I list reasons and examples explaining why an outdoors program is a good idea or a bad idea?

_____ Did I state my opinion and give reasons to support my opinion?

_____ Did I use words and details that clearly express my ideas?

_____ Do my sentences make sense?

_____ Did I check my sentences for proper grammar and punctuation?

_____ Did I check my spelling?

_____ Did I make sure my paper is the way I want readers to read it?